Confessions of a "Pick Me!" Girl

Jaleesa L. McCutcheon

Pearly Gates Publishing LLC
INSPIRING CHRISTIAN AUTHORS TO BE AUTHORS

Pearly Gates Publishing, LLC, Houston, Texas (USA)

Confessions of a "Pick Me!" Girl

Print ISBN 13: 978-1-948853-41-5
Digital ISBN 13: 978-1-948853-42-2
Library of Congress Control Number: 2022900256

King James Version scripture references are used with
permission via Zondervan.com. Public Domain.

This is a work of fiction. Names, characters, businesses, events, and
incidents are the products of the author's imagination. Any resemblance to
actual persons, living or dead, or actual events is purely coincidental.

For information and bulk ordering, contact:
Pearly Gates Publishing, LLC
Angela Edwards, CEO
P.O. Box 639
Harlem, GA 30814
BestSeller@PearlyGatesPublishing.com

Acknowledgments

I would first like to thank God. Not to sound cliché, but I would not be where I am today if it were not for Him. I am forever grateful for His grace and mercy and that He never gave up on me.

I would also like to thank my significant other/partner, Markis Steele, for pouring into me spiritually, teaching me what love is and how to love, and being patient with me.

To one of my best friends, Hybrie Bishop: Thank you for your feedback and help with naming *Confessions of a "Pick Me!" Girl*. You are one of my biggest cheerleaders, and I am thankful for having you as a friend.

Last but definitely not least, I would like to thank my family. From my parents to grandmother's blood (and not blood), brothers, aunts, uncles, and cousins…I could go on and on explaining the "why" behind each person's influence and impact on my life. Just know my family means the world to me. In everything that I do, I ensure I reflect them in the best image possible. Thank you to Mimi, my CAU village, and Nique Nique as well.

Preface

Confessions of a "Pick Me!" Girl is a fictional story about a young lady's journey towards finding love.

When the world shut down, I began writing this book at the beginning of the COVID-19 pandemic. It was always a dream of mine to write a book focused on the obstacles and experiences I went through towards finding love.

Why not pursue that desire when I had a lot of free time to do so during the height of the pandemic?

Now, I must admit: Writing this book was no easy task. There were many times I wanted to give up due to some events revealing unhealed wounds. I found myself facing bottled-up emotions I thought I had gotten over but didn't.

Then, self-doubt began to sink in. I thought to myself, "Who will want to read this book? How can I even write a book about love and relationships when I'm still trying to figure those things out?"

That was when God revealed that I didn't need to have it all figured out. I just needed to do my part and allow Him to do the rest!

The devil's tactic is to silence believers from sharing their testimonies because others receive healing from them. I encourage you not to let him win.

My prayer is that sharing my story will encourage those who are discouraged and have given up on love. Allow God to fill the void they are so desperately trying to fill on their own.

~ *Jaleesa L. McCutcheon* ~

Introduction

Come with Jordyn down memory lane as she reflects on obstacles that assist with building her into the woman she is working on becoming. With channel vision focus on becoming a wife and mother, Jordyn looked for love in all the wrong places, only to be left feeling unloved and useless.

Despite the difficulties, petty temper tantrums, and a flood of negative thoughts of never achieving her goals of becoming a wife and mother, Jordyn understood she must accept God's will for her life. She learned to let go of the fairytale image of marriage she had been holding on to and replaced it with the biblical image, all while learning to be content in every season of her life. As she correlated her experiences with those of women in the bible, Jordyn realized her journey wasn't all that different. She found their stories relatable and embraced the healing and strength needed to continue her journey.

The author of *Confessions of a "Pick Me!" Girl*, Jaleesa L. McCutcheon, ultimately wants the readers to feel inspired to love again and make room for God to do His part in their lives. Whether through healing relationships with loved ones, guiding them to their purpose, or allowing Him to pen their love story, Jaleesa believes her story will speak to the hearts, minds, and souls of all who read this book.

Table of Contents

Chapter One

Puppy Love

"Jordyn! Girl, you were the talk of the party this weekend! My homeboy can't stop talking about you. Is it okay to give him your number?" Faith asked. Jordyn was so focused on fitting in at the party, she didn't even notice any of the boys who were there.

"Sure," Jordyn replied with a bit of hesitancy. This was her second school this semester, and she had just gotten out of a relationship with her first so-called boyfriend, who had cheated on her with one of her so-called good friends. Plus, she was still adjusting to the attention she received from guys who found her attractive—something she was not used to. More often than not, she was the girl in the background who crushed on guys at school who paid her no mind.

Jordyn was pissed when she learned her mother decided to move the family from an area she had known all her life to somewhere new. As an afterthought, she mused, "This would give me a chance to revamp my image!"

Within Jordyn's previous peer group, she was known for being loud and outspoken. She noticed guys were only attracted to girls like that for "one thing" and tended to gravitate to girls who were more modest and soft-spoken to build a future with. She decided she would train herself to become more like the latter in her new environment—what society called a "Pick Me Girl."

What is a "Pick Me Girl," you ask? It is someone who pretends or tries to be different from other girls to get attention from the opposite sex.

Jordyn had a goal: to meet a guy who would become her high school sweetheart, eventually get married, have kids, and live in a white picket fence neighborhood without a care or worry in the world. In her mind, they would live "the good life." Growing up, she always knew she wanted a family of her own. She often found herself fantasizing about being a wife and mother, even while role-playing with her dolls or playing house with the neighborhood kids. Being a wife and mother was always at the forefront of her mind. Jordyn's only issue was this: She could not get married and have kids if boys did not find her attractive!

Many girls go through awkward stages during childhood. According to the Self-Esteem Project, "only 2% of women believe they are beautiful." In today's society, it is estimated that women spend approximately 45 million dollars on makeup alone. Many women will do anything in their power to make themselves look beautiful — at least according to what the "worldly" definition of beautiful means.

Hell, Jordyn was a middle-schooler who had tried any and everything she could to gain weight and develop the hourglass figure she saw on video vixens such as Melyssa Ford and Buffie the Body. She would kill to have a body like theirs: a slim waist with a plump peach booty attached. It seemed all the boys admired girls who looked like that. In Jordyn's mind, if she had that body, she could easily draw the attention of her future "Boaz" and, at the same time, find the inner acceptance she searched for so desperately.

However, looks weren't the only thing Jordyn wanted to change about herself. She was willing to give up who she was as an individual by suppressing her voice and caring more about the opinions of others, just to become the ideal girl whom boys gravitated towards.

It's funny how those same insecurities she struggled with as a child in middle school were magnified in her adulthood…

Faith and Jordyn made plans to go to a football game that Friday and, while there, Faith would introduce Jordyn to "the dude." Knowing her mother would not let her go to the game if she knew Jordyn was going to meet a boy, she did like most girls her age did: conveniently left out that detail.

The night of the game, Jordyn got herself dressed up all nice. She was nervous about meeting "the dude," but she had her girls there to support her along the way. However, no one could have prepared her for the embarrassment and humiliation she was soon to experience from "the dude," all because she did not meet his standard of beauty. What was even worse was that her so-called friends found the humiliation to be entertaining. The support she sought turned into laughter.

In today's society, girls are one another's worst enemies while, at the same time, they paint a false image of women's empowerment.

In her new environment, Jordyn learned "friends" was a word that was used loosely. All she knew about relationships was learned from her peers, romantic movies, and television shows. Her grandmother would probably lump her in with the "fast tail group" of girls if she were remotely aware of what Jordyn knew about sex.

Being in a relationship was something Jordyn greatly desired. She often found herself drifting away in romantic novels and their storylines, daydreaming it was about her. She frequently utilized her imagination to distract her from reality. It was strange for her because she could not understand why the urge was so strong and wished it would just go away.

Jordyn was raised by her mother. Her father popped in and out of her life every so often, which caused their relationship to be strained. She observed her mother's relationships with the few boyfriends she had and knew she wanted something different than what she saw emulated through their "love." Although she wanted something different, she didn't know where to start to make that change.

Once she started attending high school and stepped back into the dating scene, Jordyn dated guys just because they asked her out. There was no true connection and very little communication. It didn't help that she had no idea what it meant or took to be a girlfriend. That was a topic her mother shied away from discussing. All her mother told her came in the form of a threat:

"Don't be out there kissing boys because kissing leads to babies, and only you or the baby can come back home — and I'm not leaving a baby out on the streets!"

It wasn't until Jordyn's junior year of high school that she met a guy she had a real connection with, could be herself around, and could communicate with until the wee hours of the night. His name was Blake.

Jordyn met Blake on the last day of school. It was the end of the day, and she was headed to her bus, amped and ready to begin her summer break. She didn't really have any plans for the summer, other than spending time with her cousins and eating her mom and aunt "out of house and home." As she approached her bus, Blake stepped to her with more swag and confidence than any guy she had ever talked to.

"What's your name?" he asked.

"Jordyn. Yours?"

"Blake." They chatted briefly, and then he asked for her number, only to misplace it before he could call. *Typical teenage behavior…*

On the first day of their senior year, they reconnected. From that day forward, they were inseparable. They talked on the phone every day after school about anything and everything. During school, they were always together, skipping class and hiding out in the hallways kissing and touching. Jordyn enjoyed being around Blake. Not only did he make her happy, but she could also be her authentic self around him without any judgment. A bonus was they both shared a genuine interest in music. Blake wasn't just her boyfriend; he was also her best friend.

After a couple of months, it seemed appropriate that Blake was the first boy Jordyn brought home to meet her mother—a moment she will never forget. She disapproved of their relationship immediately.

A wise man once said, "When someone dear to you — like your family or friends — disapprove of a relationship, it makes you want to be in it even more." In that case, he was right. Jordyn was head over heels for Blake (her grandmother would say that her nose was wide open).

Blake was fun and edgy. He did things most parents would advise their children to stay away from. Like Jordyn, Blake was raised in a single-parent household and was the oldest child. One might say it was their family dynamics that brought them together.

Although Jordyn's mother disapproved of her relationship with Blake, it did not stop her from seeing him. On the weekends, she would meet up with him at the movie theater or mall, and they would spend the entire Saturday together. Both wanted to start a family at a young age and wanted some of the same things in life. Unfortunately, their relationship came to an end when Blake's family relocated. Although they were still in the same city, they lived many miles apart, making it hard for them to see one another because neither of them had transportation. The distance began to cause a strain on their relationship.

The two of them remained friends and continued to speak to one another over the phone, but as time went on, the calls that used to last until the wee hours of the night turned to every-blue-moon calls. Eventually, the calls stopped altogether, which broke her heart. Blake wasn't just Jordyn's first love; he was her friend, one of her closest friends, the first guy she kissed, and the first guy she tried to lose her virginity to. He was also the poster child of what she wanted her next mate to be.

As mentioned previously, Jordyn always knew she wanted to marry her high school sweetheart and start a family with him. Blake made that fantasy appear achievable, but once their relationship ended, she began to feel hopeless. Although she dated other guys, her connection with Blake could not be made with anyone else. She was left with watching as her peers became pregnant and lived out the fantasy she so desperately wanted to come true: starting a family with her high school sweetheart.

With senior graduation slowly approaching, Jordyn shifted her focus. The attention from guys began to wane, and those she was attracted to began to label her as "the wifey type." She found herself being overlooked for the girls who were willing to give it up at the drop of a dime. They were the ones getting the attention, and she knew she could not compete with that. She chose to place her dream of wanting to become a wife and mother on the back burner as she tried to figure out what career path she wanted to take.

Jordyn knew she wanted to go to college and be successful in life, but she was barely maintaining a 2.5 GPA. The struggle was real as she did her best to stay on track for graduation. The only job experience she had was babysitting her younger cousins and friends of the family's children—something she was good at and really enjoyed. She thought about a career in teaching and wanted to be an entrepreneur. She honestly did not know what to do and had very little guidance finding her path.

There was one girl Jordyn socialized with from time to time. Jordyn noticed her style and demeanor had changed over the past few months. One day, as they were headed to class, Jordyn noticed the girl's shoes and complimented her on them.

"Oh, girl. Thanks! I got them from my job," the girl replied.

"Where do you work?" asked Jordyn.

"At a strip club. I can get you on if you are interested."

Jordyn was puzzled and caught off-guard by her response. She didn't know what to say at first. She just knew the answer would be something different, like she worked at a shoe or clothing store. Out of nowhere, she said, "Yeah, I do need a job."

"Okay. Well, meet me in front of the school at the end of the day. You can ride with me up there, and I'll introduce you to the manager."

Jordyn was shocked! There she was, making plans to go to the strip club for the first time to apply for her first job. Sadly, she could not dance if her life depended on it. She had no rhythm nor the confidence to get naked in front of anybody. She spent the entire day thinking about what she had just agreed to. Nonetheless, she couldn't go back on her word because she didn't want to look like a punk. Before she knew it, 2:30 p.m. came, and she was standing outside of the school in the parent pick-up line with ol' girl about to get in a pickup truck with some random guy.

Jordyn wished that was the worst part of the story, but as the afternoon turned into the evening and the evening into the night, things went from bad to worse. Jordyn and ol' girl found themselves stranded at a local gas station, and Jordyn was scared out of her mind! She was more concerned about the beatdown she would receive from her mom if she did not get home soon. (Little did she know, her mom had already been up to the school looking for her and was two seconds away from calling for a search party.)

Out of nowhere, two random guys who looked to be in their late twenties/early thirties approached Jordyn and ol' girl, agreeing to take them home. Jordyn never made it to the strip club that day, but the adventure scared her straight and made her realize she wasn't built for that type of lifestyle. It was only by the grace of God that she made it home safely and that the guys who took her home didn't try anything inappropriate.

With only a few months left until graduation, Jordyn found herself lost while trying to figure out her path in life. Outside of wanting to be a wife and mother, she knew she wanted to be successful but not what success would look like for her. Everyone's definition of success is different. In her adolescent years, she didn't consider a person a success unless they had a family and career by the age of 25.

As she matured, God showed her differently.

Jordyn's fantasy of marrying her high school sweetheart never came into existence, which was truly a blessing in disguise. I mean, let's be real: 17/18-year-old Jordyn would not have been able to handle everything associated with being a wife and definitely could not endure the sacrifices of a mother. Each role came with a level of maturity she needed to develop over time.

Relationships take a lot of work. As young girls, our mothers should train and prepare us for our role and position within a relationship. It's one thing to say no to teenage dating, but it's also imperative to explain the reason behind the no — not stupid cliches, but raw, authentic, transparent moments.

Jordyn didn't need to be on the dating scene at that time in her life anyway. She didn't know who she was as an individual, she was broken, and most of all, she was unequipped. Her first mistake was compromising who she was due to others' opinions of her. If she could tell her younger self anything, it would be:

"While finding your voice, don't allow others to silence you through the process. Focus on loving yourself for who you are, inside and out. Learn as much as you can by taking risks and going on adventures."

She would also tell herself to allow God to write out her love story and not be in such a rush to piece together a make-believe fairytale that would only leave her shattered along the way. God knows what is best and has the final say, so just trust and respect His plan. It will save you a lot of heartache and disappointment in the long run.

Sadly, many young girls with a similar background as Jordyn's go through similar situations where they utilize love/lust, money/career, or try to meet expectations set by others, all to fill a void in their lives. As they transition from adolescence to young adulthood, they go out into the world with unrealistic goals and find themselves looking for love in all the wrong places.

Chapter Two

I Am a Grown Woman

Jordyn was so excited to graduate from high school! She wanted to be grown so bad, it wasn't even funny. After living a very sheltered life, gaining her independence was something she truly longed for.

After graduating, Jordyn moved out of her mother's house and in with relatives who allowed her a bit more freedom. She got her first grown-up job, was making bank, and had little to no responsibility weighing her down. Her life consisted of going to work and coming back home. She was what one would call an "introvert," spending a lot of time alone. Other times, she was with her family and friends (until they left for college).

Partying and going out were things Jordyn didn't engage in, so meeting new people was a rarity. At work, she made a few friends with whom she hung out occasionally, but work consumed a lot of her time. Plus, she was attending school at a local community college taking a course or two here and there. Outside of keeping up with some of her classmates on Facebook, she was over the guys she knew from high school.

There was one man who caught her attention at work. He worked a different shift than her and was enrolled at Prairie View A&M University. On paper, everything about him was good. He had a job, a car, was attending college, working toward his career, and on top of it all, he was a gentleman and all-around stand-up guy. Jordyn and Mr. PV began to hang out and established a friendship, but nothing too serious. Her family thought he was a nice guy and allowed him to come over, which gave the two of them more time to spend with one another.

One day, Jordyn was enjoying her day off and decided to go for a walk around the neighborhood. While out and about, a guy named Brody approached her. They exchanged numbers, and before she knew it, Jordyn found herself in a predicament where she had to make a choice: Should she continue talking to Mr. PV or ditch him for Brody? After all, the two men were like night and day.

Brody was unemployed, had no plans on attending college, and was just a hood nigga trying to make it in the world. Hell, Brody's own mother warned Jordyn about him, but Jordyn was young and naïve. Brody added spice to her otherwise dull life. On the other hand, Mr. PV was a safe bet and could probably give her the fantasy life she desired as a child, but there was something different about Brody that captured her attention. Maybe it was because he had the same edge as Blake—the poster child of her "dream guy."

In the end, she chose Brody…a choice she later had to face the consequences for.

Things between Jordyn and Brody shifted quickly. Within two weeks of dating, they became boyfriend and girlfriend. Roughly three months into their relationship, they moved in together.

The night before Jordyn moved in with Brody, she had a sleepover with her cousin Rylee. Rylee was someone she admired and looked up to—the big sister she never had. Her opinion meant a lot to Jordyn.

In typical Rylee fashion, as the outspoken person she was, she asked Jordyn, "Is moving in with Brody something you really want to do? Do you love him?"

Jordyn didn't know how to answer those questions. At that stage in her life, she was clueless about what love truly was. How could she give someone something she knew nothing about? All she knew was the dream of becoming a wife and mother persisted, and it was surely about to come true once she moved in with Brody. Based on how she felt, she believed she loved him. However, as she grew and learned what love really was, she realized she was moreso in lust than in love with him.

Jordyn's world revolved around Brody. Every time you saw him, you saw her. Her focus was solely on him. She slowly began to lose sight of what she wanted in life and was willing to settle for whatever came along with being with him, even his criminal activities.

Brody went to jail at least four times during the two years they lived together. Jordyn was floating on a sinking ship and, before she knew it, was barely passing her classes at the community college, which landed her on academic probation. At one point, they lost their apartment and were forced to move in with his mother. On top of all that, Brody violated his parole and went back to prison. Jordyn was so devastated, she didn't know what to do. She felt stuck and hopeless, knowing he would be gone for a long time.

She had a difficult decision to make: Would she be a "Ride-or-Die Chick" or pack her things and go?

For about six months, she chose to ride out his bid with him, but things between his family and her grew tense. The next thing she knew, his mother kicked her out—which was actually a blessing in disguise.

After that, life was a blur for Jordyn. She fell completely apart. She was so broken and lost, she would talk to any guy who so much as looked her way. She was desperate, insecure, did not know her worth, and was afraid of being alone. As a result, guys could do the bare minimum to get her attention. Still, she never released the hold her dream had on her of becoming a wife and mother, which was becoming her "god."

She sought to fulfill her childhood fantasy for as far back as she could recall. She wanted it so badly, she put it on a pedestal above her beliefs and values. When it became her tunnel vision, she no longer adhered to her Christian beliefs as she should have due to her lack of understanding. She didn't realize the love she so desperately yearned for could only be given to her by Jesus Christ.

Jordyn went to church because it was "the right thing to do." In her heart, she knew there was something more powerful than her or any other human being on earth. She knew about God, but she did not know Him. Her life experiences helped develop her faith and walk with God. Although she knew it was a continuous journey, she tried everything in her power to make her dream a reality, which caused so much destruction in her life.

You see, God is a jealous God. He dislikes when you put other gods above Him—something Jordyn learned later in life. Her dreams were not coming true because she kept trying to do it all on her own instead of allowing God's will to take place in her life. She would cry like a baby often, wondering why her dream had yet to be fulfilled. Was she not worthy of it? So many questions raced through her mind, but it was during those moments when she found herself drawing nearer to God and wanting to learn and know more of His Word.

There's a particular story in the Book of Genesis about a lady named Leah. Her father, Laban, tricked Jacob into marrying her. You see, Jacob initially worked for Laban with the promise that he could marry Laban's youngest daughter, Rachel. Being that Leah was not married, Laban married her off first to Jacob and then required him to work extra years in order for him to marry Rachel (the woman he really wanted). It must be noted here that it was customary for the older siblings to get married before their younger ones during biblical times.

As Jordyn read that story, she began to wonder how Leah felt in that situation. After all, she was married to a man her father had to trick into marrying her. She had no genuine connection with Jacob. Not only did he not want her, but he also purposely chose to remain a slave to Laban so that he could marry her sister. As the story progressed, Leah often felt hated by her husband, whom she bore many children for, but the intimacy she yearned for in her marriage and sense of belonging were never there.

Jordyn knew exactly how Leah felt. She, too, wanted to be loved and have a real connection with someone — not just be with someone "just because." Although Leah was married and had children, a void remained in her life…just like Jordyn's. Leah's story helped Jordyn realize that being a wife and mother would not fill that void of wanting to be loved due to it being something internal. However, it did not stop her from searching and wanting to fulfill that desire.

When Brody's mother kicked her out, Jordyn and Brody never really officially "broke up." They just stopped communicating with one another. She had gotten so accustomed to dysfunction that she became uninterested in being in a serious relationship. Plus, part of her was still connected to Brody, but that connection did not stop her from dating.

A week or two before Brody returned to prison, a close friend of Jordyn's informed her that she knew someone who was interested in her. At first, Jordyn didn't pay any attention to that information because she was still in a relationship with Brody. Once he went away, though, that changed. She told her friend it was cool for her to give the dude her number, and within a few weeks, they had a date night scheduled.

When they first met, Jordyn wasn't feeling Chase. Her interest in him was minimal at best. He was just a guy she hung out with to keep her mind off of Brody. Chase was sweet, caring, and dependable, and they built their relationship on genuine friendship. She didn't care if Chase talked to other women because she talked to other men. In her mind, they had a mutual understanding of what was going on between the two of them — until the course of their friendship began to shift.

As a whole, the situation was toxic. Jordyn went from wanting to be "just friends" with Chase to crushing on him, to a semi-relationship, to ultimately hating him. She honestly couldn't identify whether she and Chase were ever truly in a relationship, but what she did know was that he took her to a place she had never been emotionally. She never wanted to return to that place again in life.

Now, it would be foolish and unfair for Jordyn to place all the blame on Chase for how their situation ended up where it did. However, she could say she was always honest with him and never played with his emotions. She, too, played a part in how bad things had gotten between them.

When she found herself interested in pursuing a relationship with Chase, Jordyn believed it was too late. He was used to what they had going on and likely would not want to commit to anything serious between the two of them. He might have even been in another serious relationship Jordyn didn't know about. You would think she would have taken the hint when he had his first child, but she didn't. She thought they would work things out and become the blended family seen on television. Jordyn was okay with being a stepmother because, in her mind, Chase did not have a relationship with anyone outside of her, even when she sat on the sidelines while he tended to the needs and cares of his new family. Jordyn was right there waiting with open arms when he had time for her. Yes, she was foolish, but she was also young, insecure, and trying to create something that wasn't meant for her to create. She allowed Chase's double-life to take place for so long, she eventually found herself feeling embarrassed. She couldn't believe she was okay with being a side-chick—but it wasn't the first time she permitted her life to be uprooted that way.

Wait. Let me pause here and be clear: It is never okay to mess with another woman's man. Life has a way of making you reap what you sow, so best believe if you mess with a man who is not "yours" (i.e., married or in a relationship), you will have to deal with a woman messing with your man.

The day Jordyn realized things with Chase had come to an end was when the dependable, trustworthy, sweet, and caring guy she knew him to be became unrecognizable. She didn't think she would ever cry behind any guy the way she cried behind Chase. Their bond was different than the one she had with Brody. It might be because their relationship was created on a foundation built on friendship first, much like the one she had with Blake. Although both were good guys, neither was meant for Jordyn.

Jordyn found herself in a familiar place: she needed to take a break after life with Chase. Honestly, she never felt the way she did after they stopped communicating. She didn't know her purpose, and the dream she was so focused on made her lose sight of the dreams of success she had. She grew up in poverty and wanted to make something out of her life, including transferring from community college to a university. One of her good friends gave her the push and encouragement she needed to apply to Georgia A&M University. That was the best decision she made in quite some time. She learned she was accepted on her 22nd birthday.

On orientation day, she thought to herself, "Oh, no. This is not for me." The city of Atlanta within itself was different from what Jordyn was accustomed to. Plus, she was 22 years old. Most college students were either graduating or close to graduation by her age. One of the "OGs" (Orientation Guides) gave her a pep talk that included all the reasons she should attend GAMU in the fall. Her mother was on the fence about the entire situation but was there for Jordyn every step of the way while letting her know that it was Jordyn's choice at the end of the day.

Considering that she was transferring to GAMU from a community college, she only had a semester's worth of credit to carry over. That meant Jordyn had to commit to living in a different environment for about three years. That new level of uncertainty put fear in her very soul. "What are you doing?!" she thought to herself.

With courage and faith in God, Jordyn packed up her things and moved to Atlanta, Georgia. Attending a Historically Black College or University (HBCU) was another dream of her, being that she graduated from a predominantly Caucasian school district. She always wanted to go to school in a more urban setting. Don't get it twisted, though: Jordyn was from "the hood," but the teachings she received about people who looked like her only came during Black History Month. At GAMU, she was living Black history.

Going in, Jordyn didn't think she would make any friends at the university, and she was okay with that. She needed to focus on her studies because she rarely did well. Sad to say, she made average grades but wanted to do better and push herself with the new opportunity presented to her.

Her first year on campus, she lived in a dormitory called "The Suites." She had a suitemate who lived in the same space, and they had a bathroom that connected their room to two other suitemates. Initially, Jordyn thought they would not want to hang out with her because she was four years their senior. One of the suitemates graduated high school a year early and was a "baby" compared to her. Oddly enough, she saw so much of herself in that "baby," it frightened her. For example, just as Jordyn went through her early young adult years roaming and searching for love, so did the "baby." Jordyn never judged her because she was once in her shoes. Instead, she just prayed that God would protect her and lead her down a different path than the one she was on.

Jordyn spent a lot of time with her suitemate, who became her first friend at GAMU. In a relatively short amount of time, they became best friends. Jordyn nicknamed her "Gerber Baby" because she reminded her of the babies in the Gerber commercials. Gerber Baby was from the Midwest—a part of the world unfamiliar to Jordyn until Nelly busted on the scene. She was very smart, funny, and upheld a prestigious standard of living. At times, she was bougie but had a ratchet side that came out from time to time. Throughout the course of Jordyn's matriculation at GAMU, Gerber Baby was always there for her. She was one of her biggest cheerleaders and, at times, was the one who put Jordyn in her place when needed.

Jordyn continued to date while living in Atlanta, but the dating scene was way different in comparison to what she was used to in Houston, Texas. Atlanta was a flashy city, with beautiful women everywhere she looked. She could easily get caught up in materialistic things, which was why she had to find something to keep her grounded. For her, that "thing" was always Jesus Christ. She joined a local church and got an off-campus job while making sure she could balance her new lifestyle. She took classes in the morning, worked in the evening, and chilled with her friends at night. When she wasn't with them, she had a rotation of guys she went out with.

Even then, a part of her held on to Chase. She didn't know what it was about him that had her so hooked! Chase was like a test Jordyn knew all the answers to but still got them wrong. She often thought to herself, "While I'm in Atlanta trying to get my life together, I'll give Chase time to get his life together. When I return home, somehow…someway, we will end up back together." That silly fairytale ending she had created as a child all those years ago never seemed to fade, with only about a tenth of her dream of being a success coming true. Her friends told her to shake him, but she couldn't. They had a soul tie she thought would never be untied.

What is a soul tie? It is when two people come together intimately and become one. According to the Bible, intimacy is marriage. During biblical times, when you were intimate with someone, you and that person were considered married.

One of Jordyn's dearest friends she met at GAMU named DeDe was someone she connected with on a spiritual level. She was a P.K. (Preacher's Kid) who loved the Lord and wasn't afraid to show it. DeDe was a virgin and was saving herself for marriage. Jordyn admired her because that took a lot of courage and discipline. Not only that, but DeDe also had a deeper relationship with Christ — one Jordyn strived to have as well. Jordyn had practiced celibacy a few times in life but never reached DeDe's level. During that time in her life, it was easy for Jordyn not to be so wrapped up in a guy emotionally because no soul ties were being made.

With her emotions still connected to Chase, Jordyn would often find herself praying for him more than she prayed for herself. It took a while for her to become untied from him, but she no longer hated him and wished him the best when that tie was finally broken. She felt as if she were going crazy until the time finally came when she could move on with her life freely.

Chapter Three

Generational Curses

Jordyn was born and raised on the north side of Houston, Texas. She lived with her single mother and younger brother. Her mother was 19 years old when she found out she was pregnant with Jordyn and lacked the life skills necessary to take care of a baby. Her mother was the youngest of five children whose sisters had children as teenagers as well. She vowed to take a different route early on, but she was out there doing "grown folk business," so grown folk things were destined to happen.

Jordyn's birth happened in the back room of her grandmother's home. Her mother told her that she had just gotten in from work and ate a delicious southern meal prepared by her mother (Jordyn's grandmother). When she finished eating, she went to the restroom, thinking she had to "release some toxins," only to discover her water was breaking. Luckily, she wasn't home alone; Jordyn's grandmother and aunt were there with her. Her grandmother ushered her mother into the back bedroom while her aunt called 911. Being that they lived in a not-so-gated community, it took the paramedics some time to get to their home. With wisdom and courage, Jordyn's grandmother coached her daughter through the birthing process. Jordyn's aunt — who was a nervous train wreck the entire time — had the honor of naming her. She shared the name of a character from a late '80s sitcom similar to "A Different World." Ironically, the character whom Jordyn was named after attended an HBCU, just as she did in her mid-20s.

To this day, Jordyn binge-watches episodes of the show and often visualizes her birth with the show playing in the background or coming on shortly after being placed in her mother's arms for the first time.

Naming a child is an important parental task. You want to ensure their name has power and a distinct meaning or message. Jordyn believed her aunt met those criteria, which was why she loved her name and wouldn't change it for a thing in the world. Knowing where you come from and your background gives you a sense of pride and belonging. Although Jordyn knew one half of the story, she longed to know the other half.

Just like Jordyn, her mother was raised in a single-parent home due to her father dying from colon cancer when she was a little girl. Jordyn's mother rarely spoke about her childhood experiences, but the stories she did share helped Jordyn understand that her mother also felt lonely and craved love as a child. Even with that knowledge, at no time did Jordyn think her mother nor grandmother were misfit parents. If anything, both were darn good parents who did everything they could for their children.

Yes, it would have been ideal to have both parents in their children's lives, for each parent plays a different role in a child's life psychologically and emotionally. If one parent is absent due to death or other reasons, the present parent must find a positive missing component — one who can fulfill that role.

Jordyn's mother tried to do just that when she got married, but unfortunately, that union ended. Her mother's divorce was Jordyn's first traumatic experience. She recalled going to counseling at school and moving in with her aunt until her mother got back on her feet. One thing Jordyn admired about her family was how, through tough, uncertain times and hardships, they could always lean on one another. As a child,

Jordyn watched her mother work hard to support her children. Sure, they had their ups and downs, but she was and still is someone she knows has Jordyn's back through anything. Jordyn's mother is also one of the most resilient people she knows. As a matter of fact, all the women in the family were strong and opinionated Black women who didn't back down from anything.

After her mother's divorce, Jordyn observed the men her mom dated and often judged her based on the type of guys she talked to. It was disappointing to watch her waste her golden years by being in dead-end relationships time and again. There was a lesson to be learned, though. Jordyn learned that she should never judge a woman based on their experiences because one, she hasn't walked in their shoes, and two, if she did walk in their shoes, she would likely not know what to do to remedy any given situation.

God gives us free will to make our own choices throughout life, which makes each person unique. No two thought or action processes to those choices are the same.

With that in mind, Jordyn devoted much of her life to not making the same mistakes as her mother. She refused to go to her for advice about guys and shared very few details about her relationships with her. Jordyn spent so much time masking her insecurities and other things that bothered her, she suspected her mother had no idea just how much she suffered from them.

As life would have it, the harder Jordyn tried not to replicate her mother, the more she became like her. As she matured, she and her mother started having transparent conversations, which permitted Jordyn to view her mother's life story from the lenses of a woman, not a child. Think about it: Children often look at their parents as their first superheroes. In their eyes, parents have it all together and never experience pain. The reality is that superheroes do experience pain, and there are many times they do not have it all together. Once Jordyn learned and embraced those truths, she stopped trying to hide the parts of herself that were like her mother. Instead, she began to dig deeper and asked questions that were the catalyst for her own healing process. It was necessary in order to break the chains that were passed down to her from generation to generation.

What was even crazier was when her grandmother shared stories about her previous relationships with men. Those conversations helped Jordyn understand and respect her grandmother all the more as a woman. Judgment was tossed out the door, and Jordyn was able to see herself in her mother's and grandmother's stories.

Through those intimate talks with her mother and grandmother, things began to become clearer to Jordyn. She knew God wanted to do a new thing in her life that was bigger than just becoming a wife and mother. Sure, those things were going to come to pass, but she needed to be equipped for the journey ahead of her. She needed to know her role as a woman, wife, and mother and understand the biblical meaning versus the worldly definition of each.

Oftentimes, women become wrapped up more in the titles and struggle to balance each role, not realizing they are codependent of one another.

One of Jordyn's favorite stories in the Bible is the one about the woman with the issue of blood. The story is mentioned a few times throughout the Bible, including once in the Book of Matthew and again in the Book of Mark. They tell of a woman who was bleeding for 12 years due to a disease of some sort. She visited every doctor in town, but none could cure her of the disease. When she had run out of resources, she did not know what more she could do. She had heard about a man named Jesus who was scheduled to come to town, so she joined in with the crowd when He arrived. As He passed her, she reached through the crowd and touched the hem of Jesus' garment—and was healed immediately! The story goes on to say that Jesus asked His disciples, "Who touched me?" after feeling the anointing leaving out of Him. There were too many people in the crowd for the men to identify who it was. The woman with the issue of blood became nervous and confessed that it was she who touched Him. In response, Jesus said to her, "Your faith has made you whole."

What made that story so special to Jordyn and the reason it was one of her favorites was that she could relate to the woman with the issue of blood. In her heart, she believed every woman could relate to the woman. How, you ask?

Well, your issue of blood may not be a disease, but it could be anything that keeps you bound and searching for a solution. Much like the woman, many others hold on to something that keeps them bound. They turn to different things, thinking they will help them be released from bondage, but the only One who can loose them is Jesus! Our faith in Him can bring us the healing we desperately need and search for, but we must be bold and brave to go after what we want, just as the woman with the issue of blood did.

As for Jordyn's father, he was raised by his father and grandfather in Egypt, Texas, and the oldest of three children. He was a true country boy at heart.

It never ceased to baffle Jordyn when she learned the girls from the west coast were encouraged by their parents to meet and marry men from the south due to their upbringing, charismatic traits, and traditional values. When she heard that sentiment while at college, she always thought of her father because on paper, he fit that description to the 'T.' In reality, however, he did not meet those criteria — at least from what she knew about him.

Jordyn's father was an educator, just as his father was. An alumnus of Tennessee State University, he took education seriously. Perhaps that was because it was something engrained in him through his family.

Jordyn never forgot attending her first and probably only family gathering with her father's side of the family when she was a teenager. One of her aunts discussed school with her and then stated, "If you are a Jones, you have to attend college because we all obtained our bachelor's and graduate degrees." Jordyn was so upset when her aunt said that because it seemed as if she were trying to imply she wasn't "one of them." She felt as if her aunt were looking down on her.

At the time, Jordyn was unable to vocalize what it was that she felt after her aunt made that comment, but she did embrace the anger she felt. When she returned home and told her mom about the incident, she was heated and spilled the beans: Jordyn wasn't a Jones anyway! She was a Mocoyd! That was when Jordyn realized why she was so angry and feeling the way she did. She grew even sadder because her aunt's statement was, indeed, true: Jordyn wasn't a Jones. Her father wasn't present at her birth, and she didn't have his last name. She never asked why he wasn't there because she did not like talking about her absent father. In Jordyn's community, it was normal for fathers to be absent from their children's lives, so discussions about them were rarely had.

Jordyn remembered getting in trouble once in middle school, and her father popped up by sheer coincidence. Her teacher lit up when he came into the classroom and, before she knew it, she spilled all the tea about how Jordyn was misbehaving in her class. Meanwhile, Jordyn was shocked by her father's unexpected appearance. She didn't even know how he was allowed to come in because she didn't recall her mother adding him on the paperwork sent home from school at the beginning of the school year. Her teacher scheduled an emergency parent-teacher conference on the spot, which Jordyn felt was unnecessary. Once the conference was over, her father spoke with her outside — but it had nothing to do with what he and her teacher discussed. He was there to catch up with his daughter, not realizing the embarrassment and bottled-up emotions he caused inside of her.

The next day, Jordyn went to school and was sitting in class quietly doing her work when that same teacher made a smart remark about how "talking to students' parents always caused them to change their behaviors." Before she knew it, Jordyn cussed her out from top to bottom. How dare that woman — who knew nothing about Jordyn's family dynamics — make such a comment that was obviously directed at her?! In a way, Jordyn was trying to prove to her teacher that her father had no control over her. She was being rebellious.

Jordyn's father was two years older than her mother. Every time she thought about the story of how the two of them met, she laughed. The story goes that they met while driving on the freeway. It was funny because she could actually picture her father chasing her mother down on the highway, just to "holla" at her. She honestly didn't know how they stayed together long enough to make her, and her grandmother felt the same way. She could not recall a time when she was around both her parents at the same time and was oblivious to how often they fought with one another. Although she felt like they hated each other, deep inside, she still wanted them to be a loving, happy couple. Jordyn often prayed they would get back together, get married, and give her a baby sister. That never happened, of course.

As a matter of fact, her father ended up marrying someone else. Jordyn didn't find out about that woman until the day of their wedding. Her father called out of nowhere, instructed her mother to have her ready because he wanted Jordyn to be present at his wedding, and told her mom that he was on the way. Her mother was livid and refused to adhere to his command. It had nothing to do with him getting married; it was how it was presented to her. Neither Jordyn nor her mother met the woman, yet her father came out of the blue to try and paste together a blended family.

Throughout her life, Jordyn's father was consistent with one thing: popping in and out of her life. He would either come to her house unannounced or call every blue moon, making promises he wouldn't keep. He was never someone she could rely on. She thought him getting married would change things, but it didn't. What hurt her the most was that he was a stand-up guy to her two younger brothers and his wife's son.

A part of Jordyn envied them. They had the family she wanted and were blessed to live in a two-parent household. Jordyn never understood how his wife could be with him, knowing he didn't take care of her. His wife had another child from a previous relationship, so she should have known what raising a child in a single-parent home felt like.

She knew very little about her father and his wife. Plus, they had her two younger brothers whom she wanted to build a relationship with. One day, she asked her mother if she could spend the summer with her father. After speaking with him, her mother agreed that it would be fine. That year, when school let out for the summer, her father came to pick her up. She was so excited about actually going to spend the whole summer with her father!

Less than 24 hours after her arrival, she had to return home because his wife was not okay with her being there. She stated she wanted to speak to Jordyn's mother to see why she was even sent there in the first place. Jordyn thought to herself, "Why do I need a reason to be at my father's house? I mean, he's my father!" Jordyn wondered why her father didn't speak up for her. He had allowed her stepmother to make a decision that greatly impacted their lives. From that day forward, any hope of having a relationship vanished.

By the time Jordyn graduated from high school, her father had become a minister. When her mother found out, she had a load of negative things to say. Meanwhile, Jordyn was genuinely confused and could not understand how God allowed her father to deliver His Word to the people. Not long after that thought passed through her mind, she was reminded how God used many people to draw others to Him — and some did not always come from a "perfect" background.

Jordyn chose to believe that her father honestly did the best he could for her. One Father's Day, she visited his church to spend the day with him. That day, he preached about fatherhood and admitted the mistakes he made on his journey. That was the first time she saw her father through the lens of an adult, not as his daughter. Just as she did with her mother, she set aside the judgment and empathized with him. She then saw a man who was raised in a single-parent household, just as she was. He, too, was someone who likely yearned for his mother's love, just as Jordyn yearned for his.

Although Jordyn and her father didn't have the best relationship, she no longer had hatred in her heart for him. Now, she would be lying if she said she no longer envied his relationship with his other family, but her faith in God made her believe that in time, healing would restore their relationship.

It is typical for a young girl to be the apple of her father's eyes. Many tend to date guys who resemble their father (something Jordyn denied during her dating journey). Reflecting on those days, she realized Chase had some of the same traits as her father in his younger years. She was also sure the guy God created just for her would definitely share some of her father's wiser characteristics.

Her parents may not be the best and may not even win a "Best Parents Award," but Jordyn has learned to accept them for who they are. They still have their ups and downs and endure trials just like any other family, but those trials have helped them become better along the way. Who knows: They may get the opportunity to right their wrongs when they become grandparents!

Jordyn believed God wanted certain generational curses to end through her. It was He who placed a dream in her heart at a young age, but it was His grace and mercy that blocked every attempt she made to make the dream come to pass on her own. She knew she deserved better than what was presented to her in the past, so she embraced also knowing that her children and future generations would no longer be raised in single-parent households. She was going to have a marriage built on faith in God, and their union was going to last until God called them home.

The "good life" Jordyn fantasized about would come, but she first had to call out the demons that were holding her family hostage. It took Jordyn a while to reach that epiphany. Although she still battled within herself at times, she knew that God would have all the glory for the good things He had done in the end.

Chapter Four

Homie, Lover, Friend

As Jordyn approached her mid-twenties, her focus was on making sure she obtained her bachelor's degree and that she had a job lined up in her field after graduating. She knew she did not want to remain in Atlanta due to it being a fast-paced city. It was not a place for someone like her to settle down and start a family. Perhaps the broader truth was she didn't feel confident that she would meet a man who only had an interest in her and would be willing to settle down and start a family. There were men she was good friends with and attracted to for varying reasons, but she didn't have a romantic connection with them — something she made a point to let them know. She hung out with them to occupy her time, but it was never anything serious.

One day, while looking for a place to stay off-campus, Jordyn and three of her girlfriends were approached by a group of guys. Their names were Levi, Landon, and Connor. After introducing themselves, the men gave Jordyn and her friends a tour of the rowhouses they were looking to sublease. Jordyn thought to herself, "These guys would make great realtors!" The men were down-to-earth and easy to talk to, and from that day forward, became the ladies' protectors throughout the remainder of their stay in Atlanta. If they needed anything, they could reach out to the guys, and they would always come through for them.

One of Jordyn's friends in the crew named Imani could throw down in the kitchen. Her suitemate, Gerber Baby, was the best baker she knew (outside of her family, of course). Every Sunday after church, the ladies would come together and enjoy a meal while discussing the latest gossip and their future. They also spent that time encouraging and uplifting one another. The tradition became something each looked forward to. Many of their roommates envied their closeness and camaraderie. Somehow, word got out about their Sunday dinners, and the guys started inviting themselves over to join them. During those times and many others, they often had healthy debates about any and every topic imaginable. Just as the guys had their backs, the ladies had theirs.

Levi and Landon were brothers who played football for GAMU until Levi got injured one night during a game. Feeling without purpose, he dropped out. He and Connor were neighborhood hustlemen. Everyone went to them when they needed something and knew not to mess with them, but to the ladies, they were fun to be around.

Jordyn often came home late from work because she had to take public transportation, and it would be dark outside. Connor would often greet her and, depending on what was happening at that moment, he would walk her home to make sure she arrived safely. She could always count on Levi or Connor being on the block handling their "business."

Being the homegirl who kept it real at all times and didn't play any games, Imani warned Jordyn that both Levi and Connor had a thing for her. Jordyn paid her no attention because they were all cool and like family to her. After all, both men had plenty of females they talked to. Plus, she didn't look at either of them like that. From her perspective, they were gentlemen who looked out for those they cared about.

One day, Connor was at the wrong place at the wrong time and found himself in some serious trouble that got him sent to prison. The group of friends was saddened but tried to stay positive. Meanwhile, Levi started to date someone he was really interested in, which drew him away from the group. Jordyn found herself feeling a little salty because he stopped talking to her altogether once he got into his new relationship.

Jordyn couldn't quite pinpoint how and when she and Levi began talking again, but she did know when their relationship resumed, something fueled sparks, and they began to bond on an intimate level. Through that bond, she saw Levi past the persona he put on. He was someone searching for love, just as she was. They were both broken and available to comfort one another when needed, but Jordyn found herself in that familiar place again: stuck and not knowing how to get out. The consistency of that cycle was becoming overwhelming.

One day, Levi dropped Jordyn off at work when a guy pulled up next to them at a stop light. Levi pulled out his gun and placed it in his lap, frightened the guy might do something harmful to them. The incident that sent Connor to prison left Levi with post-traumatic stress and paranoia. As for Jordyn, she was petrified and didn't know what to do when he pulled out his gun. She knew he carried it with him at all times, but she wasn't prepared to be caught up in any situation with him.

It seemed as if Levi was living in a daze. At night, he had trouble sleeping, along with the fact that he was self-medicating, attempting to fight off the demons that taunted him. The two of them spent a lot of time together while he was going through it, but Jordyn could do nothing to help him. He needed professional help to get through all that he was dealing with.

Things between Levi and Jordyn began to get shaky when she found out he told Connor they were a couple, which was a bad time to share that bit of news because Connor was still in jail, dealing with a lot of his own mental, physical, and emotional struggles. Although Jordyn remained in contact with him, she still viewed him as one of her homeboys and nothing more. As such, it was normal for her to check in with him and see how he was doing. Connor also remained in constant contact with Imani as well. They spoke daily, and it was Imani who told Jordyn that Connor knew about her and Levi. Connor then said he no longer wanted Jordyn to reach out to him. Jordyn's heart sank to the bottom of her stomach when Imani told her that.

Jordyn felt so betrayed by Levi that she confronted him immediately when she saw him again. Just like the lying nigga she suspected him of being, he denied telling Connor anything. She was heated and distanced herself from Levi from that day forward.

Once alone, Jordyn found herself thinking about the events that led up to that moment. Perhaps Imani was right: Both Levi and Connor had a thing for her. Was she so naïve that she didn't see what was obvious to others? Yes, she and Connor would playfully flirt from time to time, but it was never something serious (at least in her mind, that wasn't the case). There she was, trapped in a three-way love affair that she had no idea existed! Disappointingly, she lost a true friend over something that really wasn't anything at all. To top it off, she was scheduled to move within the next month or so.

Before Jordyn left Atlanta, she had a procedure scheduled that she had been putting off. The day before, she went to the facility to get blood drawn. A few hours later, she received a call from the doctor informing her that the blood test read positive for pregnancy.

"No, I'm not. You must have misread the results," Jordyn stated confidently.

"I'm sorry, Jordyn, but the results are correct," the nurse responded. "Due to these results, we are unable to proceed with your procedure. Please reach out to your primary doctor to follow up with a pregnancy test."

Jordyn was speechless. It was as if she went blank for a moment.

"What's going on?" DeDe asked Jordyn.

Jordyn came back to reality. "Girl, that was the doctor. Why did she just tell me I'm pregnant?!"

"WHAT???" screamed DeDe, whose voice was naturally loud. "That's good news! We must celebrate! That means you are going to have to stay in Atlanta!!!"

Jordyn could not process what was going on. She knew her body better than anyone. Nothing had changed. There was no way she was pregnant! "Pump your brakes, DeDe. There is no guarantee that the results are correct. Next week, I will make an appointment to confirm whether the results are accurate. Until then, keep your mouth shut, and let's act like this conversation never happened."

Thank God it was Friday and Jordyn had the day off. She decided to spend some time alone and sort out her thoughts. As the weekend progressed, she started to feel pain in her lower abdominal area. She was also spotting, but it wasn't like her usual menstrual cycle. Suddenly, she began to feel ill and spent the remainder of her weekend in bed.

Luckily, she was able to see her doctor first thing Monday morning, where she later learned she'd had a miscarriage. When she heard that, she was in more denial than when she received the call about her pregnancy results. She just couldn't believe any of it. She never felt pregnant, nor did she have any symptoms. When she expressed her concern and disbelief, the doctor explained to her that it was because she was in the early stages of her pregnancy. It took Jordyn a while to understand and accept that she experienced a miscarriage. Not only that, but she also hadn't told Levi about anything that took place. The only person who knew was DeDe.

"You have to tell him. It's the right thing to do," said DeDe.

"I don't know. I mean, there's no child coming now, so why does it even matter?" Jordyn resisted.

"Why? Because it's his experience as well," DeDe countered.

Jordyn allowed a couple of weeks to go by before she told Levi about the pregnancy and miscarriage. He nonchalantly asked, "So, if you didn't have a miscarriage, what would you have done?"

She gave him the side-eye and asked, "What do you mean by that?"

Levi shared with Jordyn about an incident with his previous girlfriend. She, too, happened to get pregnant by him and was convinced by her family to get an abortion. Jordyn hoped he wouldn't expect her to do the same thing. After all, all she ever wanted in life was to be a wife and mother, and she wasn't going to do anything to jeopardize that. Although unmarried or even in a committed relationship, she still would have done whatever it took to care for their child.

Perhaps that was why God didn't allow the pregnancy to go full-term. He knew that becoming a mother would change Jordyn's whole world, and that wasn't something she was ready or prepared for.

She held onto her secret for dear life. However, her mother sensed it. Call it her "woman's intuition" or just her "motherly senses," but she somehow just knew. Jordyn would ignore her when she commented about it and quickly changed the subject. The loss of her baby was something Jordyn couldn't accept and come to terms with, especially knowing her mother also had a miscarriage with her first pregnancy — a story she only shared with Jordyn. If anyone could relate to what she was going through, it would be her mother.

Oftentimes, we (as humans) mask our pain, hoping it goes away on its own rather than talking about it and seeking the help we need.

As time moved on, Jordyn often found herself daydreaming about how her life would have been had she not had a miscarriage. Would she and Levi still be together, even if just for the sake of their baby? She believed everything happened for a reason and that only God knew the answer to that question. She didn't understand things at that time, but they became more apparent as time went by.

A couple of years later, Jordyn was in a different stage in her life when she received a text from Imani stating Connor had died. As she read and re-read the message, she was so confused and thought to herself, "This can't be real! Maybe Imani sent this message to me by mistake." Later that day, she spoke with Imani over the phone and was provided more information on Connor's death. Jordyn was at a loss for words. She hadn't spoken to Connor ever since his request for her not to reach out to him anymore. She was heartbroken and wished she could have spoken to him one more time, just to give him some type of support and encouragement. Imani also informed her that Levi had reached out to her during that same call, asking about Jordyn. He told her to have Jordyn give him a call.

Per his request, Jordyn called later that day to check on him and see how he was handling the situation. You see, once she left Atlanta, she stayed in contact with Levi due to them being friends. As time went on, those once-in-a-while check-ins came to an end. It was never her intention to be in a relationship with Levi. Neither did she intend to hurt Connor. Honestly, she looked at both of them as two of her many male friends. She would have handled things differently if she could have gone back in time. Hurting Levi and losing Connor were two of the only things in life she wished she could have changed completely.

Once accepting of all that happened in her life, Jordyn shifted her focus to her career. She told herself, "Whoever God has for me, He will send him my way." It was funny: She never really went searching for guys; they seemed to always appear out of nowhere. With the pressure of fulfilling her dream on the back burner, she vowed to no longer give time to situations that did not lead to anything serious.

As millennials, dating is a task all its own. There are no rules for dating in our generation, which causes a lot of chaos, confusion, and constant battles between the sexes. There is little to no commitment between two people who come together and partake in activities that are dedicated to couples. It's easy to get wrapped up in what we call "situationships" or "friends with benefits." Far too often, one party is left feeling distraught and lost once the other has decided to move on with their search because of boredom or the desire to find someone better.

Jordyn and countless other women have fallen victim to that many times, leaving them to wonder what it is they've done wrong. As women, it is not in our genes to be with someone physically and not become attached to them. In today's society, we are taught that women and men are equal when, in reality, that is not true. God did not make us equals. In fact, He put rules in place for us in His Word that clearly show how we should conduct ourselves as men and women. For example, the Book of Leviticus speaks about women who partake in "whorish" activities and how the community should treat them.

Jordyn had two close childhood friends named LaTavia and LeToya. The three of them were like "The Three Stooges." Every time you saw them together, they were laughing, joking, and being flirtatious with the guys. It was just innocent, naïve fun. However, as they entered adulthood, life took each of them through different journeys—ones neither of them wanted to take but had to due to the choices they made in life.

LaTavia moved back to their hometown, where she ended up settling down with her husband and two children before the age of 25.

Meanwhile, Jordy and LeToya were in Houston, trying to figure life out.

One day, LeToya and Jordyn were talking and reminiscing about the times the three ladies used to hang out. LeToya stated when she last spoke to LaTavia, she advised her never to get married. That caused an outburst of laughter between Jordyn and LeToya.

You see, LaTavia was a social butterfly who enjoyed life to the fullest and was a joy to be around. Being tied down to any one man was not her "flavor." Plus, on top of all that, she was very beautiful. Guys always gravitated to her, but she paid them no mind. Her being the first to become a mom and wife was a shocker. Becoming a young mother was not on her agenda, but it was definitely something she needed to slow her down, which led to her marriage.

That is something that happens to many women, especially when they become careless. It is often best to date and live your life. The man of your dreams will come when God knows you are ready to receive him into your life.

As for Jordyn, she wasn't built to be emotionally attached to a guy. She was an emotional person by nature but could not feel for someone she was casually talking to. However, she did an excellent job of masking it while in their presence. Once she was alone, those emotions got the best of her, and she learned what worked for others didn't work for her.

Eventually, Jordyn went on a "man fast." For about a year and a half, she refused to entertain any man. She used that time to focus on obtaining her master's degree. She also worked on her relationship with God and birthed her spiritual journey. Now, she would be the first to admit it was challenging because she hated being alone. During the process, she was alone all the time. She had moved to a new environment where she didn't know anyone and really didn't care to make new friends because she knew she wouldn't be there long. There were times she wanted companionship, but the sacrifice had to be made. She would either settle for someone who would only be around for a moment or wait for someone willing to be around for a lifetime.

Chapter Five

God's Plan

For some reason, turning certain ages in our society is a big deal, with 25 being one of them. On Jordyn's 25th birthday, she woke up that morning feeling down. She typically didn't go all out for her birthday. It was normal for her to spend the day alone, treat herself to an outfit or two, and grab a bite to eat with lots of treats. Being that her birthday fell on a Sunday that year, she was up early getting ready for church. As she fixed her hair and applied her makeup, she decided which outfit she would wear for the day. The outfit she chose to wear to church that day said, "I'm a grown woman who has it all together," although, in her heart, she knew she didn't.

Growing up, Jordyn always thought that by the age of 25, a person had to have their life together, meaning they had to be working in a field they enjoyed or tolerated enough to go to every day, making a living to support themselves and/or their families. They had to have a place of their own to call home, reliable transportation, and a family of their own (if that was a desire).

That explained Jordyn's gloominess. On her 25th birthday, she felt like a failure because she had none of those things. Hell, she was still struggling with trying to figure out her life, and it was getting the best of her!

By the age of 25, society tends to look at you as an adult. They expect maturity and you to have a sense of what you want out of life.

Jordyn knew what she wanted her life to look like, but she didn't know the steps needed to get her there. Everything she had done up to that point was apparently wrong because she was nowhere near where she wanted to be. She was fed up and wanted to throw in the towel. There's an adage that states: "If you want to make God laugh, tell him your plans." Jordyn felt God was laughing hysterically at her plans — the kind of laughter that made your belly hurt from laughing so hard.

When Jordyn arrived at the church, her spirit was immediately uplifted. There was something about attending church and being in the presence of God that did something to her. Everything was going well until Bishop came forward with the message, which was titled "It's Time to Grow Up." Jordyn's eyes filled with tears instantly, and she boohooed the rest of the service. The message hit home. It was as if her pastor was speaking directly to her.

It was time for her to grow up mentally, physically, and spiritually. She claimed to be a Christian, yet she did the bare minimum. Yes, she attended church every Sunday, streamed Bible study every Tuesday, and was even active in the college ministry. She faithfully sowed her first fruit and paid her tithes as often as she could. Still, Jordyn trusted God to handle only a fifth of her life. She believed if she played her part, He would reward her based on her participation while trying to do the other 95% on her own.

Jordyn left the service that day feeling worse than she did that morning. It felt as if the tears were never going to stop falling that day. She decided to go see a movie called "Baggage Claim," thinking that would cheer her up — but that movie was basically her life story.

She thought to herself, "If God loves me so much, why is he allowing me to go through so much pain? I don't understand what is going on. I know I'm not perfect, but some people do things way worse than me, yet they are better off than I am!" Her thoughts went deeper. "Maybe it's not in my destiny to be a wife and mother."

Just then, God began to speak to her and show her visions of a woman and man standing at an altar reciting their vows and, later, an image of a baby girl. In the quietness, the Holy Spirit said to her, "You are worthy of these things. I am preparing you for them. Just trust Me. Remain faithful to My process and My timing."

Society would have you believe that if you do things by the book or in a certain way, your life will flow smoothly. That's not true. Life is not a cookie-cutter. Everyone is placed here for a reason, and we will all leave this earth at different times. What works for one may not work for another. You can do everything right, and things will still go wrong because that's just how life is.

One of the Fruits of the Spirit is longsuffering. In the Bible, there's a man named Job who lived an upright lifestyle, but he lost everything to the point that his wife was like, "Look, bruh. This God-thing ain't working. You need to give up on Him." However, Job remained faithful through it all, and, in the end, he received God's glory.

In the Book of Jeremiah 29:11, it states, "'For I know the plans I have for you,' declares the Lord. 'Plans to give you hope and a future.'" God formed us in our mother's womb. Of course, He knows what is best for us. He knows everything about us. He knows when we are hurting, sad, and happy. God gives us free will to do whatever we want. Sometimes, we may not make the best decisions, which causes us the hurt and pain we endure. That is why our relationship with Him is so important. Through that relationship, He guides and directs us. Instead, we often choose to "do life on our own," which may come from us not knowing or understanding Christ's purpose in our lives.

People fail to tell others that once you turn 25, time seems to fly by. It should be no surprise that she was deep in her mid-twenties before Jordyn realized that things were getting even crazier.

Jordyn found herself missing Atlanta, so she decided to take a trip out there for the New Year and spend some time with her girl, DeDe. They agreed to attend Watch Night Service for New Year's Eve but couldn't decide which church to go to, so they hopped from church to church.

While at one service, a prophet prophesied to Jordyn, telling her the upcoming year would be the one where she received everything she asked God for. Jordyn began to pray like crazy!

That same week, while she was getting her hair braided, the stylist told Jordyn she would meet her future husband that year.

Jordyn was like, "Okay. I don't know what's going on, but I'm going to trust what's being spoken over my life."

That year, Jordyn was shown a lot of favor. She was delivered and healed while attending a women's conference. She received her master's degree—an accomplishment she could only obtain by God's grace. Still, she had her fair share of hardships. She lost the only father figure she had, just as they were repairing their relationship. Then, on top of that, she had to share a secret with her mother that she had been holding onto since the age of 12 about a neighbor who sexually harassed her. When she told her mother about the abuse, it was like a weight had been lifted off her shoulders. However, the look on her mother's face was heartbreaking.

"Why did you wait so long to tell me?" she asked with a slight quiver in her voice.

"Honestly, I don't know why. I wish I had the courage to tell you when it happened. For some reason, I chose to keep it to myself. Perhaps I was hoping you would notice how whenever he was around, I stayed near to you and had no contact with him." Her mother looked so hurt and confused. She left the room without saying another word and went to spend some time alone. The subject was never brought up again.

Jordyn often wondered if her abuser did the same thing to other young females or maybe something even worse. She also wondered if telling her mom when it happened would have changed things or would it have been swept under the rug like many secrets within Black families and communities.

As time progressed, Jordyn believed that year wasn't the one when she received everything she wanted, but it was a year of breakthroughs and healing. She knew it was all a part of God's plan to heal her from the hurt she had suppressed and to allow her to release the baggage she carried for so long.

During that time, Jordyn spent a lot of time by herself and began to take her relationship with God more seriously. She had removed herself from the routine of participating in the many weekly activities in the church and worked on developing a personal relationship with God. She learned that she needed to know God for herself because there were times she reached out to her pastor, and she was unable to help due to their conflicting schedules. Jordyn had to learn to pray for herself and seek God on a different level. At one point, she thought she should have sought professional counseling to process everything but knew God was the best counselor ever. He was there with her through the whole healing process.

However, she did have one friend she could confide in during the process. One day, she was venting to her friend about all she was going through when, out of nowhere, thoughts of her biological father forced their way to the forefront of her mind. At the time, his ministry was growing, but due to the strangeness of their relationship, Jordyn felt as if she could not go to him for advice, direction, or anything else. That hurt her more than anything. Her friend advised her to look at her father as her spiritual leader, not her birth father, but Jordyn's pride wouldn't allow her to be that vulnerable — something she was constantly battling. As well, she wasn't sure if she and her father would ever have the father-daughter relationship she yearned for as a child, but it was something she prayed her own daughter would have with her father.

Jordyn thought back to the night her aunt — the same one who named her — passed away. That night, she prophesied that Jordyn would marry someone of great status and that she would be the one to break their family's generational curse. It was as if God Himself was speaking through her. Jordyn knew she had a significant assignment in her life to complete but always operated on a mediocre level. She knew God had big plans for her — bigger than anything she could ever imagine — but in order for her to receive any of what He had in store for her, she had to learn how to move out of the way and understand the life she lived didn't belong to her: it was God's. She also had to learn how to be obedient to what He asked of her, even when she didn't understand or want to do it. She had to admit to herself that there were times when she didn't want to do what was required of her to get to where she wanted to be. She tried her best to compromise and act as if she no longer wanted what she had been asking and begging God for due to a lack of knowledge and understanding of what she needed from Him.

The visions Jordyn had about marriage and a baby girl kept coming. Eventually, she asked God to stop showing them to her because it had become overbearing as she thought about them and tried to paste together how to live out the visions and make them her reality. Although she knew God had nothing but the best interests for her, there were times when all she thought about was when her time would come to be a wife and mother. She often went to bed at night with those thoughts, and it sometimes felt like she was under attack because they consumed so much of her thought processes. Out of frustration, she went back to trying to do things the way she saw fit.

One guy she knew had the biggest crush on her while they were undergrads. Jordyn never paid him any attention because he never made an effort to approach her outside of the call girl remarks he made when he saw her. One day, she was scrolling through a social media site when she came across his profile. She sent him a friend request, he accepted, and they began talking and building a friendship, which soon led to them dating casually. At one point, Jordyn thought to herself, "Maybe this is the guy for me. And to think: There I was, the whole time in undergrad, passing up my husband who was right in front of me!"

The devil sure was slick with that one, though. That guy was not Jordyn's husband, although he did have some of the traits she wanted in her husband. Conversely, he also had many traits she didn't want, but she was willing to overlook them because, in her head, he was "the one." Surely, it wouldn't get any better than him! Out of desperation, she was willing to settle for "less than the one."

Meanwhile, God was like, "Look here, Jordyn. You said you wanted someone who loves Me and seeks after Me, will treat you right, is faithful, and wants to build a life with you. You are the one who continues to date and talk to guys whose character doesn't match up to any of those things. Your actions are not lining up with what you are asking Me for, and you are steadily yoking up with men you are not easily yoked with."

In a nutshell, Jordyn was causing herself so much pain due to her trying to put together what she thought her love story should look like instead of allowing God to do it.

Ladies, listen up: As women, it is not our job to look for a man. The Bible clearly states, "He who finds a wife finds a good thing." So, once we learn to fall back and allow the men to do the "finding," it will cut out a lot of confusion and unnecessary heartache.

"Okay, God: I surrender," Jordan professed for the umpteenth time. That time felt different, though. She had truly gotten to the point where she didn't have any more time, room, or energy to make more bad choices. She was in her late 20s, beginning to get settled in her career, and wanted the next phase of her life to be dedicated to building her family. She vowed from that day forward, "Every choice I make, I will consult with God before doing anything and move only according to His will. If it is not a part of His will for my life, I don't want any part of it."

Living for Christ is not as easy as it may look or sound, especially when you have become accustomed to moving and doing things your way. More often than not, your choices are not based on logic but moreso on how you feel. For example, in this story, if Jordyn didn't feel like doing something that wasn't a life-or-death situation, she didn't do it. Now, some might say she was a very selfish person because she believed the world revolved around her. If things didn't go the way she wanted them to, she would back out of doing them altogether.

Jordyn learned from her pastor that feelings are fickle— meaning one minute, you feel happy, want to help everybody, and do any and everything humanly possible. The next minute, you find yourself feeling sad behind something someone said that upset you, and all the gusto you had to help others had disappeared. In response, you would rather be left alone to watch Netflix at home. The bottom line is this: When you make decisions based on your feelings rather than logic, it creates chaos and confusion, neither of which is healthy.

God's plan for His children is to live a peaceful life with no worries, even when we go through difficult times. As for

Jordyn, He knew that going to school, having a successful career, and becoming a wife and mother was just the icing on the cake. He also knew she wanted her children to have a better life than her own and that she desired a marriage that would last until death did them part. God had already designed her marriage to be one that would represent what a Godly marriage truly looked like. Together, Jordyn and her husband would build something that helped God's Kingdom. They would raise children who came from order, knew what love looked like, and would not need to go searching for it or seeking acceptance.

"This is what you have been crying about and asking Me for, and I am willing to give you the desires of your heart whenever they line up with My purpose for you. Until you allow Me to strip away the things that are not of me, I must hold onto them." Those were God's words spoken directly to Jordyn.

Trusting God's plan is a process. Fighting against it causes your life to lead to destruction. You would think it's so much easier just to follow God, but sometimes, He is silent and leaves you unsure of what He wants from you.

Jordyn was in that stage of life when God finally yoked her with the man He created just for her. She was fearful of the damage she could bring to herself and the relationship if she didn't do things God's way, so she insisted He shows her everything He wanted her to do.

Chapter Six

What is Love?

What is Marriage?

Jordyn found herself back in the cycle of being over the dating scene. She was just beginning her master's program and decided she would dedicate the next year and a half towards focusing on that. However, her flesh was weak. She wasn't built like those self-proclaimed feminist women. Not only did she want, but she needed the companionship of a man in her life. Jordyn knew she needed a man, and although she was embarrassed to admit as much amid the male-bashing conversations, she still had hope that her Boaz would find her.

For so long, she held onto the false image of what love and marriage looked like ever since she was a young girl, including the fairytale images she saw based on Disney characters in movies or those she read about in storybooks. Then, there were the images she had based on what her mother's, aunt's, and friend's parents' relationships looked like (if they were blessed to live in a two-parent household). Most of the images were misleading due to them not covering the reality of what love and marriage really were.

Jordyn laughed to herself as she reminisced about the naïve conversations she had with friends about how she envisioned her marriage would be. She dreamt of marrying a professional football player or someone in a leadership position who owned their sense of power. Together, she and her husband would run the south and give back to underserved communities. They would be a powerful couple who lived in a gated community with their three beautiful children. Her husband would help her fulfill her dreams of opening a nontraditional charter school and spoil her with a monthly allowance that she would use to keep her hair and nails done. Most importantly, she wanted her husband to love her unconditionally, just as she was ready and willing to do for him. Jordyn held onto that unrealistic image of what she thought her marriage would be like well into her mid-twenties.

People marry for various reasons such as love, financial security, or title. Jordyn wanted to get married for a combination of them all. She wanted someone who loved her more than she loved herself, the security of being in a committed relationship, and a man who was willing to spoil her like the princess she was. Being a wife versus a girlfriend brought with it a different status quo in society, and that was a title she knew she deserved and was going to wear like a badge of honor.

In Jordyn's home library, she had many books that focused on the topic of love and marriage, from the famous *Act Like a Lady, Think Like a Man* book written by Steve Harvey that was later made into a movie, to Pastor Terrence Johnson and First Lady Torsha Johnson's *The Answer* (they were the leaders of her church). She also read different blogs on how couples met and would oftentimes try to imitate all the stories she had read. For example, if someone said they met their husband at church, Jordyn made it her agenda to scope out guys while attending church service. If they said they went a certain period of not dating, she would go that same amount of time without dating while hoping and praying that when her "man fast" ended, God would magically present her Prince Charming.

She didn't stop there, though. Part of her weekly routine included checking Essence.com to see their recently-married highlighted couple. She often visualized herself being featured on their site one day, although she was well aware that what those women went through on their journey of love was different than the one God had designed for her. No matter how much she tried to imitate or follow other couples, what worked for them was not going to work for her.

The time came when Jordyn began to get discouraged and believed maybe marriage wasn't something God had in store for her life. She reflected on the people in the Bible who never married whose lives were dedicated solely to serving God. Perhaps that was Jordyn's purpose: to serve her Creator. As if to confirm those thoughts, her pastor would somehow find a way to mention a rendition of the following during service:

"While you are in your singleness, use this time to serve God and be committed to doing things within your church or community."

So, Jordyn did just that. When she had time, she would serve at the church and volunteer to assist during events, but the desire to become a wife and mother never truly diminished. She knew only God could purge her from focusing so much on wanting that fairytale life.

Have you ever wanted something so badly, only to realize you were not ready for what it was you asked for? It took Jordyn a long time to see that although she wanted to be married, she was not quite ready for it. She was unequipped and still maintained the image of what she thought marriage looked like. In her entire life, she had only known one couple whose marriage was even remotely close to what she desired for herself. Sadly, she barely knew what love was and what she needed from a significant other.

Growing up, Jordyn was never told, "I love you." She believed that was where the yearning and desire for love within her came from. She knew her family loved her, but just like most kids who were raised in a single-parent household, she never received the attention and affection she needed. As a result, when she began dating and getting into serious relationships, she did not know how to give the guy she was with any love or affection outside of intimacy. She always made sure to tell them she loved them, but her actions didn't reflect those words.

If they did not call her, she would not call them. She put minimal effort into creating a solid relationship or even staying committed to one man. She was afraid to show them her vulnerable side — the side of her that was desperate and in need of someone to love and protect her. Behaving in that manner kept Jordyn at a standstill within her singleness. She could never pinpoint what the issue was, but an urging in her soul kept tugging at her.

1 Corinthians 13:4-5 states, "Love is patient, love is kind. It does not envy, it does not boast, it is not proud. It does not dishonor others, it is not self-seeking, it is not easily angered, it keeps no record of wrongs." That is God's model of what love is. His Son, Jesus Christ, is the image of what love is. Once we learn how to reciprocate love in His way, we can give and accept love's true meaning.

In 2014, a reality show titled "Married at First Sight" premiered on Lifetime Network. The show focused on between four to seven couples matched by relationship experts who specialized in various fields such as counseling and ministering. The couples had eight weeks to build a genuine connection with one another and determine if they would stay married or file for a divorce.

Jordyn became intrigued by the show. She thought to herself, "Who would marry someone they didn't know? Those people must be desperate!" Still, she admired how courageous they were to take a leap of faith on their quest to find love.

She recalled how, out of nowhere, a commercial came on that telecasted a casting call for the show's next season. Without giving it a second thought, Jordyn reached for her laptop and proceeded to the website to begin the application process. What did she have to lose? She was single, the dating scene no longer worked in her favor, and she was creeping up on age 30.

Interestingly, that was not the first time Jordyn considered allowing skilled, licensed individuals to match her up with someone. As a matter of fact, in other countries such as India, China, Pakistan, Japan, Israel, Afghanistan, and Iraq, most of their marriages were arranged. Some may think, "What's the difference between an arranged marriage and being matched together by licensed matchmakers?" Well, according to the Oxford Dictionary, an arranged marriage is planned and agreed to by the families or guardians of the bride and groom who have little or no say in the matter. Whereas when a licensed matchmaker matches you, you have a say-so in whether or not you want to be in a relationship with the person you are matched with.

It was common for fathers to choose their daughters' husbands during biblical times based on common factors that may connect them to one another. Those factors included wealth, culture, ethnicity, or gaining power and respect. That was common in earlier generations, but women became more involved in choosing whom they married as time progressed.

Unfortunately, Jordyn never got around to completing the application for "Married at First Sight." Plus, she honestly didn't think she would have been as brave as those who participated in the show. However, it must be noted that over the course of ten seasons to date, 30 couples have been matched on the show. Out of that number, only 12 are still married.

The thought of her fairytale marriage ending in divorce never crossed Jordyn's mind. She always said that once she got married, she would stick it out to the end. Disappointingly, not everyone holds marriage in high regard as it is intended. According to the American Psychological Association, "about 40-50 percent of marriages in America end in divorce." NewIdea.com states the divorce rate among arranged marriages is about 6.3 percent.

Millennials view marriage differently. They are more opposed to gender roles and believe that a relationship should be equal, which makes it hard for a woman to be submissive to a man without thinking he's trying to control her. In older generations, it was commonplace for women to stay in a marriage and focus on their role as a wife without being easily distracted by outside factors such as jobs, opinions of others, etc. Many millennials are oblivious to the thought of marriage or even wanting to get married in their later years versus when their grandparents might have gotten married in their early young adult years. Then, you have those who are opposed to marriage altogether. As you learn the history of matrimony and see how it is done in other countries, along with God's intent for marriage, you come to realize the worldly image of what marriage is supposed to look like is a bunch of bull.

Just as before, when Jordyn finally let go of the fairytale image she had of what marriage was, the desire and desperation slowly faded away. In their place crept in fear and anxiety. She actually feared the thought of marriage and not ever getting married due to her being unworthy of a mate who wanted to marry her. Would she meet the requirements it took to be a wife? She couldn't even get into a committed relationship to find out! She thought to herself, "Maybe being single is the best thing for me. I can continue hanging out with the guys I'm cool with and procreate with someone who was okay with the idea of co-parenting."

That was nothing but a trick of the enemy! The devil's tactic is to destroy the family, often by removing the father or mother from the home and leaving the child to be raised by a single parent. Another tactic is having people stray from wanting to be in a relationship with no desire to get married. He plants negative thoughts and ideas in their heads to make them feel like they are not worthy or deserving of the things they were created for and once desired.

That applies not only to relationships but also to any area of one's life.

Chapter Seven

Worth the Wait

It was Gerber Baby's wedding weekend, and Jordyn was excited! Someone was finally getting married and experiencing true love.

Gerber Baby asked Jordyn to be a bridesmaid, and, of course, she said yes. She really didn't understand what her role as a bridesmaid was, other than being there to support her girl as she walked down the aisle. Jordyn made sure she was physically and emotionally available for whatever came Gerber Baby's way that weekend.

Gerber Baby's wedding was the first grown-up wedding Jordyn attended. That weekend was a lifetime experience she would never forget. Gerber Baby — being the selfless person she is — decided to give her girls (Jordyn, Imani, and Jade) background information on the groomsmen while also trying to play matchmaker. Out of nowhere, Gerber Baby told Jordyn about a guy her husband was close friends with.

"Jordyn, I think you and him would make a good couple," she commented while pulling up his Facebook page to show Jordyn his picture.

Jordyn thought to herself, "I didn't come here for that. I am here to support my girl. That's all." By that time, Jordyn was really over the dating scene. Her focus was on her career and building a better life for herself. She even thought about becoming a foster mom and eventually adopting a child (and siblings, if that were the case).

That weekend, the girls enjoyed one another's company as they joked and took great pleasure in the festivities that led up to Gerber Baby's big day.

On the day of the wedding, Jordyn met her Boaz — the guy Gerber Baby had given her the rundown on…Stefan.

"May I have this dance?" he asked.

When Jordyn looked up, she saw the finest man in the room talking to her. He had swag and confidence. "Yeah," she replied. He took her by the hand and led her to the dance floor.

Jordyn couldn't dance to save her life. She had two left feet, but that didn't cross her mind until she was on the dance floor, nervously praying she didn't step on his feet. Once the dance was over, she returned to her seat thinking, "What in the hell just happened?" She and her girls chatted it up, and, within a few minutes, Stefan approached Jordyn again. That time, he asked for her number, which she gave without a second thought. That man left her speechless. She felt as if she were living a scene from one of the fairytale books she read as a child. That night, she prayed to God, asking if it was His will for something to happen between them and if so, to allow it to take place as He saw fit.

Jordyn returned home on a high. However, she didn't want to overthink things. She and Stefan lived in two different states, after all. She wasn't sure what could come from their meeting, but she remembered her prayer and promised to allow God to make His move.

A few days later, Stefan finally sent Jordyn a text. They went from nonstop texting to speaking on the phone until the wee hours of the night. Eventually, he made plans to visit her.

Jordyn didn't know what to do. A man never flew out of state to come to see her. She wished Chase had done that while she was in Atlanta, but he never did — yet Stefan was ready to book a flight to see a woman he barely knew.

The first thing she did was plan some activities for them to do while he was in town. She wanted to do something fun but also wanted some romantic events to take place. As she planned, she was in disbelief that he was actually coming to see her!

The day she picked up Stefan from the airport, Jordyn was a ball filled with mixed emotions. She focused on keeping her composure as they made small talk on the way to the hotel. She was pleased when he maintained the same level of charisma as the day they met.

Stefan and Jordyn spent a total of five days together. She had never experienced the chemistry the two of them shared with any other guy. They laughed often, had deep conversations, and realized they wanted the same things in life. Before they knew it, they were officially boyfriend and girlfriend. Jordyn was shocked when he asked her to be his girlfriend. She hadn't been in a relationship in years, but it was as if things between them were moving quickly yet so perfectly. Just as Jordyn was searching for love, so was Stefan. When both allowed God to take the lead, He brought them together and fulfilled that desire within them.

Although separated by distance, they communicated via text and phone calls constantly, getting to know one another better. At one point, Stefan suggested they read The Songs of

Solomon together—a love story within the Bible. Over the course of two weeks, they discussed each verse.

The Songs of Solomon is a love story about Solomon and an unnamed woman. Solomon is well-known throughout the Bible for his wisdom. His parents were David and Bathsheba. His mother gave him an outline of what characteristics to look for in a woman when finding a wife, which many Christian women refer to as "The Proverbs 31 Woman." Apparently, Solomon believed many women met the criteria because he was married to about 700 women and had hundreds of concubines. As such, it is unclear which woman, in particular, he was writing back and forth to in The Songs of Solomon.

In the Bible, The Songs of Solomon is eight chapters of dialogue between a man and woman who express their love for one another through poems. Throughout the scriptures, they tell how they are physically attracted to one another and are on the hunt to find each other. Some believe it isn't just a story about romantic human love but rather that it demonstrates Christ's love for the church. Love is a gift from God and something we all search for in one another.

Without a doubt, Jordyn knew Stefan was the man God designed just for her. It was with him that she would get all she wanted in life.

They long-distance dated for the next 11 months, flying back and forth to see each other when time permitted. They knew they loved each other and were committed to spending to rest of their lives together, so the time came to take their relationship to the next level. By their first anniversary, Jordyn decided to move in with Stefan.

That wasn't her first time living with a significant other. So, when she broke the news to her family, they thought to themselves, "Not again!" Jordyn knew she was a hopeless romantic, but she could honestly say that time around, she knew the man she was dating and had been with him long enough to make such a big decision (at least that's what she believed). She was at a stage in her life where she had no more room for error in her life. She could no longer afford to make bad decisions. She knew she was ready for marriage and to start a family. With Stefan, it was her chance to finally pursue her dreams.

Meanwhile, she prayed she wasn't making a decision solely out of desperation and that what she felt in her heart was truly God's divine plan for her life.

The relationship with Stefan changed drastically after they moved in together. Jordyn wasn't sure if it was because they were learning more about each other on a deeper level or because they spent all of their time together. The only other person she knew in her new environment was Gerber Baby, but she was a newlywed and beginning her next phase of life. Out of respect for Gerber Baby's marriage, she only hung out with her when Gerber Baby reached out and had the time.

Jordyn soon found herself falling into depression. It seemed as if she and Stefan were constantly at odds with one another. Both felt as if they couldn't express themselves fully due to not wanting to hurt or offend the other, which often led to an argument. At times, Jordyn wasn't even sure why he was still with her. To her, it seemed as if he was unhappy with her.

Their relationship began to feel like a never-ending rollercoaster ride. Things would go great for a few weeks, and then, out of nowhere, things would turn bad. She didn't know what to do. She had no one to talk to about what was going on, leaving her feeling lost and alone. Jordyn believed she made the right decision to move in with Stefan, but at that moment, clarity seemed far off. She knew she couldn't just give up and run back home because, in her heart, she still believed God put them together. If she gave up on the relationship, she would also be giving up on God and what He had in store for her.

All of that shifted when Jordyn learned Stefan no longer believed in the sanctity of marriage. She felt as if God Himself betrayed her. He knew how badly she wanted to be a wife, yet He yoked her with someone who didn't have the same desire after all. She masked the pain by refusing to discuss the change in circumstance, acting as if she was unbothered, and agreeing that it was something she no longer desired either. Deep inside, she was broken. The thoughts of her being unworthy to be a wife began to ease their way back into her mind.

She then found herself in the throes of spiritual warfare. It was as if God and the devil were fighting over her mind, and she didn't know what to do. She couldn't sleep at night due to the bad dreams and soon began to resent Stefan.

Jordyn had a critical decision to make about their future, so she made up her mind to give their relationship a couple more years. If things didn't change, she planned to leave him. Ironically, Stefan always made it clear to her that "he wasn't holding her hostage." That infuriated Jordyn. She always knew he didn't need her, and when he made those types of comments, it made her feel unwanted—something she needed to feel within her relationship.

Yes, Jordyn needed to feel needed. She always knew something was screaming at her soul, and that was it. She wanted a family of her own because she knew just as she needed them, they would need her as well. When she recognized just how essential that facet of very being was, she took a trip back home by herself for a couple of months to figure out why she needed to be needed.

While there, she learned that she desired to be needed because of the codependent relationship between her and her mother. One thing Jordyn could always count on was that when she went home, things were always going to be the same: her mother would boss her around and throw a temper tantrum if things didn't go her way. They would be like two peas in a pod until tension rose between them. Jordyn never understood why their relationship was that way until she paid close attention to her mother's and grandmother's relationship. She just knew that she was striving to make a better life for her family, yet she never even bothered to ask what "better" looked like to them.

During that time apart, Stefan and Jordyn began to miss one another. That spark between them returned and, when Jordyn decided to return to him, things were good…for a while.

One day, they got into one of the most heated arguments ever. She hated conflict, yet they were constantly at each other's throats. They actually cursed and yelled at one another to the point where Jordyn screamed that she was done! She was over everything that happened between them and had been stretched to her limit. What more was there for her to do?

Without thinking, she packed up all her things with no plans on where she would go. She was too far away to simply run back home. Although they were not in a good place at that moment, when things were good, they were good. She knew they were meant to be together, but she had a hard time dealing with the stretching and molding God was putting her through. Jordyn knew He was developing her into the woman He called her to be for Stefan.

Fortunately, Stefan was a stand-up guy. He gave Jordyn some time to cool down, and when they both came to their right mind, they talked things out and chose to fight for their relationship.

Chapter Eight

Daddy Issues

It was about four years since Jordyn last saw her father. When she received an invitation from him to his pastoral installation service, it happened to be the same weekend Stefan had planned to visit her for the first time. She wasn't sure how to handle the conflict in her schedule.

Before then, her father made many attempts towards reaching out to her, but Jordyn wasn't ready to mend their relationship. She was still hurting from the pains and broken promises he had fed her for so many years as if she were just some trick on his roster. She had no trust in her father because he had shown her years ago what type of man he was. Yeah, he might have truly changed, but she only knew him from his past and wasn't ready to accept the man he was working on becoming. She knew she didn't need that type of person in her life.

While at dinner the first night Stefan was in town, Jordyn mentioned the invite to him, hoping he could provide her some guidance.

"It's up to you. I'm down for whatever. Just know I am here if you need me," was his reply.

Interestingly, that made Jordyn feel some type of way. Outside of Chase, she never had a guy trust her in her most vulnerable moments. She thought to herself, "What the heck. Why don't I just go? I have someone here who's willing to support me through this journey. Plus, what do I have to lose?"

That Sunday, Jordyn woke up a nervous wreck. She was about to see her father for the first time in years. On top of that, she was bringing someone along on the journey whom she barely knew. She decided not to let her father know she was coming to his installation, so he was surprised when he saw her in the congregation. He immediately left the pulpit and came to where she was. Jordyn was filled with mixed emotions, with anger taking the lead. So, when he asked her to come to the front of the church to sit with the family, she immediately turned down the offer.

Jordyn found it difficult to concentrate throughout the ceremony. It was hard for her to sit and watch as her father was celebrated as some "good man of God." Before the ceremony ended, her father acknowledged her in front of the congregation, which embarrassed her. She thought to herself, "Typical him." It was customary for her father to paint a picture of them having a perfect father-daughter relationship when, in reality, it was nonexistent.

Once service was over, Stefan encouraged Jordyn to go and speak to her family before she left. That was the first step towards Jordyn's and her father's healing process. After that event, they continued to communicate with one another via text every so often. When she sought direction on if she should relocate to where Stefan lived, she reached out to her father for advice. She sensed her father had a high level of respect for Stefan based on their conversation.

On Father's Day that year, Jordyn spent the day with her father. She informed him about her plans the day before. The next morning, she visited his church, and, upon arrival, the same mixed emotions that accompanied her at his installation service presented themselves again. Something within her spirit was uneasy. When her father preached his sermon, she understood and gained some perspective on why he was an absent father.

You see, Jordyn never knew her dad's side of the love story between him and her mother. It never crossed her mind to ask him about it, but he often reminisced on it when he was around her mother.

Just as she did with her mother, Jordyn took a step back and stopped looking at her father as just her father and looked at him as a man. When she did that, she was able to see his story. He was a young man in school, trying to figure out life. Due to poor choices, he ended up in a situation he wasn't ready for. He handled it the best way he knew how and, as things got hard, he stepped away. Maybe he did so because he felt it was the best thing to do for his child. As he grew into the man God called him to be, he yearned to mend the relationship between him and his daughter.

Jordyn couldn't help but weep at the revelation because although she understood his story, she still blamed him for the hurt she endured. However, she knew the time had come for her to take accountability for her part in the hurt as well. Her bad decision-making and poor choices caused her to continue feeling and enduring the pain and suffering she experienced.

She thought back to a story she read in the Bible about Tamar in 2 Samuel 13:10-14. In the story, Tamar was raped by her brother, Amnon. "And Amnon said unto Tamar, 'Bring the meat into the chamber, that I may eat of thine hand.' And Tamar took the cakes which she had made, and brought them into the chamber to Amnon. And when she had brought them unto him to eat, he took hold of her, and said unto her, 'Come lie with me, my sister.' And she answered him, 'Nay, my brother. Do not force me; for no such thing ought to be done in Israel: do not thou this folly. And I, whither shall I cause my shame to go? And as for thee, thou shalt be as one of the fools in Israel. Now, therefore, I pray thee, speak unto the kings; for he will not withhold me from thee.' Howbeit, he would not hearken unto her voice: but being stronger than she, forced her, and lay with her."

Tamar was devastated after that incident. She had another brother named Absalom, who took her in and killed Amnon for what he did to Tamar. The rape plus the killing of Amnon caused a strain on the family's dynamic, but Tamar's story didn't end there. She endured so much hardship from losing both of her husbands, to having to pass as a prostitute, to tricking her father-in-law into sleeping with her to impregnate her so that she could get what was rightfully hers.

When Jordyn learned about Tamar's story, so many questions entered her mind. Never in the story did they mention anything about how Tamar's father, King David, felt when he learned about the incident between her and Amnon, other than how he was torn and didn't know how to handle the situation. Being a woman, Jordyn automatically thought about whether Tamar's feelings towards her dad changed, knowing he didn't try to punish Amnon after learning about the rape — or did he learn about the rape only after Absalom killed his brother? Even if that were the case, why did he set specific orders in place for Absalom after discovering the reason why he murdered Amnon? Jordyn wondered if Tamar resented her father and if so, was she able to forgive him?

Jordyn wished those details were provided within the story. She believed doing so would have been an excellent guidance tool for young women like herself who struggled with daddy issues. It could have taught women how to forgive their fathers and move on from the hurt that resided in them, thinking they were the cause of their father's absence. Furthermore, it could have encouraged them by relating to the cause as to why their father wasn't there to protect them, watch over them, and be their first example of what a real man looked like.

Jordyn knew she had to forgive her father for what he had done if she wanted to make it into Heaven; she just didn't know how. It was easy to say she forgave him, but those hurt feelings revisited her once his name was so much as mentioned in a conversation.

Most girls tend to gravitate towards dudes who resemble their father and share similar characteristics. In Jordyn's case, she dated two guys who were a reflection of her father: Chase and Stefan. Of course, she didn't come to that realization until years later when she received a text from Chase out of nowhere. She was furious and couldn't understand why he reached out to her almost ten years later. After all, both were in different stages in their lives. She was content in her relationship with Stefan, and her main focus was on building a life with him. Jordyn despised social media but kept a "spy account" open for situations such as the one presented. She immediately looked up Chase and, based on what she saw, he didn't need to be reaching out to her. He had two kids with the woman he "got caught slipping with" while he and Jordyn were in a situationship. She thought to herself, "I guess some people just never change," although she really hoped that one day, Chase would get his life together and become the stand-up man she knew he could be. If not for her, at least for the next woman. Most importantly, she would like to see him be a better man for his children.

The same hope she had for Chase, she also had for her father. She hoped and prayed that one day, her father would love her and become the stand-up man he was to her brothers. God heard her prayers, but she was so focused on the past, it hindered the future of her and her father's relationship.

One day, Jordyn and Stefan were having a deep conversation in which he mentioned something along the lines of, "Until you can get past your daddy issues, you won't be able to accept love from anyone."

Jordyn had to admit he was right.

She was in a relationship with a man she had prayed and cried so desperately for, for what seemed like a lifetime. He was a stand-up guy who genuinely loved her and pushed her to become the woman God called her to be—but she could not reciprocate the same love. Those daddy issues always showed up in her relationships with men, and she knew she had to do something about it. It was time for her to take the steps necessary to heal and mend the relationship with her father, not just for herself but also for her relationship with Stefan and their future children. The generational curse that had them bound had to be broken. The man her father had become was a mirror image of the man God had destined her to be with. Stefan and Jordyn's father had the same vision for their lives.

Jordyn knew she wasn't the only person who suffered from daddy issues. It was a relevant topic that was constantly swept under the rug, leaving her without the solution on how to forgive her father and move past the hurt. She actually thought about reaching out to Iyanla Vanzant to fix her life, but she knew she would have to involve both of her parents on the show for the process. She could easily envision her mother punching Iyanla in the face as soon as she called her out on her "stuff." She also considered seeking professional counseling, but it was challenging to find a professional with a biblical perspective.

There were so many things Jordyn wanted to accomplish. She had dreams of opening a mentorship program where she could help young girls who suffered from low self-esteem and needed guidance on their journey through life. She knew she could help those girls by sharing her story and life experiences with them, but in order for her to help, she first had to help herself.

Jordyn knew God wanted to use her as an example of how He can transform a broken, lost individual into a healed, walking-with-purpose individual. She couldn't just tell those girls any ol' thing while she was out doing the opposite and suffering from the consequences in silence. That would have made her a hypocrite. Most importantly, she knew transparency about her healing process and daddy issues wasn't going to only heal her, but through the process, she would be able to help other girls who battled those demons as well.

Chapter Nine

Learning to Trust the Process

Once Jordyn worked past her daddy issues, another hurdle awaited her: letting go of how she thought things should play out in her life — an issue she thought was already resolved.

In her mind, she thought that once she and Stefan got together, they would be married within a couple of years, and within their first year of marriage, they would pop out a baby. That's what she was programmed to believe would happen based on culture and the worldly way of doing things. Plus, it seemed as if everyone around them was either already married and working on starting a family, engaged, or having a baby. Jordyn found herself becoming jealous. "When will it be my turn?" she asked herself. Within that same breath, she had to check herself. "With that type of attitude, how do you expect God to bless you? Your time will come. Just remain patient and learn how to be content in your season."

She spent so much time focused on what was next that she never stopped to embrace where she was at the moment. It was as if she was trying to prove something, which was where the conflict within herself came from. Then, it dawned on her: Would she operate in the same manner when she became a mother? Would she continue to move on to the next goal on her list once she became pregnant and birthed her child, or would she embrace her motherhood journey? She took a moment to seriously ponder the answers to those questions. She had a vision for her life but was unprepared for what was to come along with that vision. She would eventually have to make some sacrifices, with one of them likely revamping her vision.

As women, we are programmed to think we can have it all and do it all, which might be true for some. However, Jordyn knew what it felt like to feel unwanted and lonely as a child. In no way did she want her kids to experience those same feelings.

Jordyn had already accepted the fact that Stefan didn't believe in the "worldly" way of marriage. He explained how, based on the Bible, he believed they were already married due to them being physically intimate with one another. She wished that had been communicated to her beforehand, as that was a battle she refused to fight. Her mother always told her, "When a man tells you something, believe what he says because there is no changing his mind."

The type of love she experienced with Stefan was unlike any other. She truly believed he was the man for her. They both knew they wanted to spend the rest of their lives together, so naturally, Jordyn felt there was no better time than the present to start building. Her biological clock was slowly ticking, and there was no doubt in her mind she wanted to be a mother. That was a dream of hers since she was a little girl. She recalled playing house after school with the neighborhood kids, and she was always the "Mama" who held her baby dolls in her arms and had a pillow under her shirt to make it appear as if she were pregnant. Motherhood was a dream she wouldn't allow anyone to take from her. "Hell, childbearing is what makes a woman a woman," Jordyn thought to herself. She also knew she didn't want to force the issue with Stefan. She never wanted any man to feel like she trapped him into becoming a father. He had previously mentioned that he had a specific way he wanted his children to be raised, and she wasn't sure she could meet those standards.

One day, Jordyn came across a minister's YouTube channel. He spoke about how women have shifted their focus from being helpmates to their spouses to focusing more on their careers. Within his segment, he said something along the lines of, "Women should not be waiting to have babies in their 40s and 50s." Jordyn immediately tuned him out when she heard that and reflected on her life. That was not the first time she listened to a message of that nature. There was another minister she had started watching faithfully and whom she respected who once stated, "Young women are straying away from getting married because they feel they don't have anything to bring to the table." He went on to say, "That is an issue because there are women who believe they need to be successful in order to get married, which has created the man versus woman culture within this generation."

Once again, Jordyn found herself reflecting on her life. She asked herself, "Am I playing a role in this battle of the sexes?" As she thought deeper, the following thought came to mind: "The only reason I attended college was that my dream of marrying my high school sweetheart never came true." She was tired of paddling around in a pond full of frogs, praying and hoping one would magically spring into her Prince Charming.

As far back as she could remember, she always made it clear that her main goal in life was to become a wife and mother, but while she waited on God to manifest those things in her life, she focused on what she could control: creating a better life for herself and her future family. Although she ended up swamped in debt, she gained new experiences, developed friendships that opened her eyes to change, and prompted her to think outside of the box. She found herself sticking to her alumna motto: Make a way or find a way when adversity hits.

It was never Jordyn's goal or plan to have children in her later stage of life. She thought she would have had at least one or two by the age of 30, but it was obviously out of her control. She wasn't purposefully trying to put all of her focus on her career, but it seemed to be the only thing she seemed to have some sort of control over.

Out of nowhere, Jordyn burst into tears. "Am I the cause of this?" she asked herself. She constantly uttered a prayer: "God, please show me Your will for my life."

One night, Jordyn had a dream. In it, Stefan held a snake that appeared to be hissing. He found it to be funny, but it frightened Jordyn. The next thing she knew, he started chasing her around with the hissing snake in his hands. Jordyn jumped up out of her sleep, horrified.

A month or so later, she had another dream where she was lying down, and a dog of some type kept rubbing against her as if it were trying to wake her up or get her attention. It kept doing that until she screamed for it to stop. That was when she woke up.

A week or two later, she dreamt of sheep. They were scattered in a field, and she caught a whiff of a weird odor in the atmosphere.

The strange dreams continued to come, with each crazier than the last. Jordyn knew one way God communicated with people was through dreams; however, the messages He tried to convey to her through them were unclear. Oftentimes, she would awaken from a dream and Google its meaning, hoping to gain some type of clarity through the translation. She even tried explaining her dreams to Stefan, who, at times, would give his interpretation of the ones he could. Meanwhile, the dreams haunted Jordyn, and she tossed and turned throughout the night.

On top of having those dreams, Jordyn still had visions of a baby girl from time to time. That excited her because she believed it was a God-given vision in which God let her know: "Look, I haven't forgotten about your prayers and the desires of your heart. You will be a mother." The visions gave her hope but also took her to a delusional place. She became obsessed with the thought of being a mother and had several Pinterest pages dedicated to photoshoots she dreamed of one day doing with her child, gender reveal party ideas, etc., etc. She would window shop online for baby clothes and nursery items, too. When the vision of her baby girl came to her, she would oftentimes try to make out the child's face and allow her imagination to create a story of her daughter and future siblings.

Eventually, Jordyn found herself unsure about those visions. Were they a product of her own thoughts and dreams, or were they actually confirming something coming from God? Worse yet, was it the devil playing tricks with her mind? She wished she could just sit with God and have a one-on-one, real conversation with Him. She desired clear insight and direction on His will for her life and what He was trying to communicate through her dreams. She was getting tired of guessing and getting it wrong, although she knew and understood that her life did not belong to her and that her purpose was to live out

God's will for her life. Jordyn knew she needed to repent and asked God for forgiveness for the bad choices she had made in the past.

It's human nature to put the blame on others for a poor decision or judgment we made rather than take ownership and accept the consequences that come with them. Jordyn knew she would not be able to accept God's will if He chose to for her not to be a mother. She even told Him, "If that's the case, You can just call me home now!" She had a legit, grown-woman temper tantrum! Being a mother meant so much to her, more than the idea of being a wife.

Imagine her disappointment when it appeared she was being asked to let go of that idea as well…

Jordyn began to question her ability to be a mother. "Can I really bear a child? I hate pain!" she thought to herself. "Would I even be a good mother? Yes, I work with kids, but who's to say my own children would even like me?" So many thoughts and questions flooded her mind, to the point she just said, "Fine, God. I'll let go. I will find contentment in whatever Your will is for me." However, just as she didn't know how to really forgive someone, she was also unclear on how to seek God's will.

As humans, we sometimes believe God is some magical being who shows up like a genie in a bottle when, in reality, He is a spiritual being living inside of us. He speaks and gives us direction through His Word (the Holy Bible), which is why, as believers, it is imperative that we constantly read the Word of God and connect with the right people. God often uses them to help guide us along the way.

The point was not lost on Jordyn. She immediately dove into the Word of God—an attempt she had made several times before, but something was different that time. She actually learned from His Word and saw herself in certain stories. A trend she saw among the women in the Bible was how God gave them insight into His vision for their lives. Instead of waiting and allowing Him to direct their paths, they took matters into their own hands, which created problems that could have been avoided. "Why isn't this being taught in churches?" she thought.

In today's society, women are not taught how to be Godly women. We often hear pastors refer to "The Proverbs 31 Woman." However, do we really know who that woman is?

Jordyn felt she was striving to be a Godly woman in a world full of "Baddies." There were many examples of how to be a baddie in the world, but little to no examples of how to conduct oneself as a woman of God. Even those trying to be an example either displayed some traits of Jezebel or, as time went by, were perceived as hypocritical because they said one thing and did another.

The derogatory name "whore" came to mind when Jordyn heard the name Jezebel. Growing up, that was the term she heard older women call women who displayed sexual characteristics. It wasn't until her relationship with Stefan and her learning God's Word for herself that she learned Jezebel had the same traits as a feminist: She wanted to be in control and out of God's order. God did not intend for women to be the head. That role was designed for men. Although the world was moving away from God's order, the church's job was to teach and keep that order at the forefront of one's mind and way of living.

Jordyn wanted to be that example. However, she knew she still battled with the expectations of the world and God's expectations. She didn't want to be a hypocrite.

One of the reasons God extends grace is so that we can extend that same grace to one another. In our humanness, we all fall short, but once we learn how to stop passing judgment, hold each other accountable, and be there to pick up one another when we fall, only then will life become a little easier.

There is a song by Jekalyn Carr called "Greater is Coming" that Jordyn enjoyed listening to. The song talks about how God takes us through different stages. He shakes, beats, and presses us—a process similar to that of an olive—in order to get their oil to flow. Each stage is necessary. We cannot skip one stage and move on to the next. It's also important not to rush one stage to get to the next. The purpose of the whole process is to prepare us to walk in the full potential God has created for us.

Jordyn knew she was called to be a mother, whether through ministering to young girls through her mentorship program or physically giving birth to a child. She believed wholeheartedly it was a part of God's will for her life, but there was still some shaking, beating, and pressing she needed to endure.

For far too long, she had taken her own routes along her life journey, hoping and praying it would lead her to the right path. The time had finally come for her to rely entirely on her faith in God to help her remain faithful and committed through those stages. Proverbs 3:5 states, "Lean not unto your own understanding, but in all your ways, acknowledge God."

Jordyn may not have understood why she was still in the "waiting room" of her process, but if she continued to seek God and learn how to hear Him for herself, she would learn how to appreciate and be content in that room. She needed to be prepared for whatever came next.

Chapter Ten

Happily Ever After

One afternoon, Jordyn was having a conversation with her mother. Suddenly, her mother bombarded her with questions about her life.

"So, what are you planning to do with your life?"

"Are you going to stay where you are and settle down with Stefan?"

"Are you and him planning to buy a house one day?"

"When are y'all going to have children? Is that something you have discussed? I mean, let's be real here: You aren't getting any younger."

Before responding, Jordyn thought to herself, "Hell, I know that! And what do you mean, 'What am I planning to do with my life?' It's not like I'm just out here not doing anything for myself and living recklessly!"

Instead of speaking those words aloud, she simply replied, "I don't know." Jordyn used that phrase frequently. It was her way of avoiding those difficult conversations with family and friends. It was also her reality. She really didn't know when those things would happen.

All the questions her mother asked, Jordyn thought about often. However, she knew those things were out of her control. She had to rely on her faith and belief, knowing those desires would come to pass in God's timing — if they were His will.

Sometimes, before a flight lands, the pilot is instructed to remain in what is called a "holding pattern" while awaiting permission to land. That is when the plane remains in the air and flies a specific route near the airport until the aircraft can touch down. During that process, passengers may become frustrated because they are close to their destination but cannot get off the plane.

That is how Jordyn felt. She believed she was in a holding pattern. It was as if her desire to become a wife and mother was literally dangling in front of her, but God kept making her wait for some reason. She was often frustrated with being stuck in that "place." The little progress she made no longer mattered to her. She was ready for the manifestation of her dreams.

There's a woman in the Bible named Hannah (you can find her story in 1 Samuel 1:2-2:21). Hannah was married to Elkanah, who had two wives: Hannah and Peninnah. According to the Bible, God closed Hannah's womb, which caused her to be unable to conceive. However, Peninnah was able to bear Elkanah many children. The Word went on to say that Hannah's circumstances put her in a state of depression. She wouldn't eat and constantly cried, worried, and was filled with anxiety.

One day, Elkanah asked Hannah, "Why are you so down? Is our marriage not enough for you?"

Hanna left and went to the temple, where she poured out all of her cares and emotions to God about how she was feeling. She was determined to stay in the temple until she got direction from God on how to handle her situation properly.

Her prayers changed from emotion-centered to purpose-centered to God-centered. She began to be so wrapped up in the presence of God that her demeanor changed, to the point that a priest approached her, assuming she was drunk. Hannah let the priest know she wasn't drunk but had been talking to God and was caught up in His Spirit. The priest apologized and asked God to bless her.

Before Hannah knew it, she was pregnant with her firstborn. Just as she had promised God, she gave her son back to Him because God was going to use him for something mighty. God didn't just bless her with one child; He blessed her with five more! You see, Hannah had experienced a holding pattern but shifted her state from being depressed to crying out to God.

Although Jordyn's and Hannah's situations were different, Jordyn could still relate to her story. She understood how it felt to want something and not know if or when she would ever get it. Jordyn had cried at the altar, too — many times — and fasted, yet she was still waiting for God to answer her prayers and bless her, just as He did for Hannah.

Jordyn couldn't figure out what she was doing differently from Hannah. Yes, she had difficulties being fully transparent to God by verbalizing and expressing exactly how she felt. She never wanted to offend God or make it seem as if she was ungrateful for where He had brought her from to where she was. After all, God blessed her with a man who had not only everything she wanted but also everything she needed. Jordyn believed she and Stefan would do something amazing for God's namesake. That was the good thing about God: He didn't need Jordyn's words to tell Him what she needed or what she was going through spiritually and emotionally. He already knew it all; He just needed her will to align with His.

The difference between Jordyn's and Hannah's prayers was that Hannah handled her situation as a righteous woman should. She never "went off" on Peninnah or her husband. She didn't try to bribe God or throw temper tantrums. Her prayers changed from what she wanted to what God wanted for her. Most of all, God conquered her heart through the process.

As for Jordyn, she kept saying she was seeking God's will, but her actions did not align with what she said. She was constantly falling back into wanting things to go her way. After all, she had been under the programming of the world longer than her walk with Christ. Just as God wanted to conquer Hannah's heart, He wanted to do the same for Jordyn.

She needed to start preparing herself for the things she asked God for, but most importantly, she needed to learn how to quiet the voices of others and spend time in silence where she could hear clearly from Him. Jordyn believed through that process, she would get direct instructions and answers from God.

As young girls, we are given a false image of what a happy ending looks like, whether through Disney movies, fairytale books, or romantic movies. Many girls rebel against the image or attempt to imitate it, not knowing it cannot be replicated because happy endings are unrealistic.

If you think about it, you never really know how things end when a romantic movie comes to a close. It leaves you guessing or painting together an image of how you think their lives will end up.

Jordyn was so focused on creating a happy ending to her love story that she was missing out on the key ingredients and special instructions needed specifically for her relationship with Stefan.

A "Happy Ever After" ending is make-believe. Marriage is real, but a biblical marriage between a man and woman is key. It is a commitment between two imperfect people who become one flesh, working towards perfection. There are several references to the bride and the church throughout the Bible. The relationship between the church and Christ is the reflection of marriage.

As a church-goer, you attend church to learn more about God, fellowship with other believers, and be held accountable. While you are learning and spending more time in God's Word, you should apply those learned skills to your everyday life. Yes, you may fall short and repent. In the beginning, it may seem challenging to stay on the straight and narrow on your walk with Christ, but as time goes by, it becomes easier when you learn to lean and depend on God because you realize He's always there.

You must go into a romantic relationship with the end goal of marriage with that same mindset.

The beginning stages of a relationship typically start off all lovey-dovey. Two individuals meet and agree to go on a date. From there, if a light is kindled, the elders would say,

"Their noses are wide open." Once that phase is over, they must choose to either stay together and work through whatever differences may come or go their separate ways. The easy way out is to give up, but stop and ask yourself:

"What if Christ so easily gave up on me?"

In addition to preparing for what she asked God for, Jordyn also needed to pray for the endurance to keep pushing, no matter what obstacles came her way. She needed to hold onto her faith and remember that God was in control. Not only that, she needed to remind herself that God didn't need her help. Her pastor, Terrence Johnson, once said, "When you run, you get ahead of God. When you stop walking with God, you fall behind Him." She had to stay on the same pace as God and wait on Him.

As millennials, we often want things to come quickly, easily, and fast, but when they come to us that way, they are lost just as quickly, easily, and fast as they came. We utilize a microwave relationship model as an image of how our relationships should look. That is a false reality—a false notion that only serves to set us up for failure, which contributes to the high divorce rate in our society and to a generation of individuals who don't want to get married.

Women who are still hopeless romantics get picked apart and criticized for doing the work necessary for a relationship to be successful.

Jordyn had to learn to quiet the noise of others' opinions, judgments, and so on. The only people's voices who mattered were God's, Stefan's, and hers. There were still some behaviors and habits she needed to unlearn and replace with things under God's rules and fit the needs of Stefan. She had to release some traditions and goals in order for God to come in and move in her life as she wanted.

She was blessed with the man she needed and, together, they were going to do something amazing for God. She no longer cared about the idea of how she envisioned her life to go. The plan and story God had designed for her was more than enough. The tears she used to shed due to pain and heartache, she chose to instead shed for excitement and joy in anticipation of what was to come.

Yes, there were still some things she wanted to do and some goals she wanted to achieve, but she was living in God's time and knew those things were going to come to pass as He saw fit. Jordyn resolved that she would be alright if they never came to pass.

If Jordyn could do it all over again, there are some things she would change and others she would keep the same. Why? Because it was those moments and scars that helped develop her into the woman she is today and the woman God is molding her to use for His glory.

About the Author

Jaleesa L. McCutcheon is a Houston, Texas native and the prime definition of a "Southern Belle." She has 15 years of experience working with children in a variety of settings, including mentoring and individual and group counseling.

Jaleesa holds a bachelor's degree in Social Work from Clark Atlanta University, and a master's in Social Work with a certificate in Family Practice from Tulane University.

Confessions of a "Pick Me!" Girl is Jaleesa's first book. For any inquiries, she may be reached at: jlmccutcheon7@gmail.com.

Made in the USA
Middletown, DE
22 February 2022

61459081R00070